Essential Maths

Book 7S

Michael White

Elmwood Press

First published 2008 by
Elmwood Press
80 Attimore Road
Welwyn Garden City
Herts. AL8 6LP
Tel. 01707 333232

British Library Cataloguing in Publication Data

© Elmwood Press
The moral rights of the auther have been asserted.
Database right Elmwood Press (maker)

ISBN 9781 902 214 757

Numerical answers are published in a separate book (ISBN 9781 902 214 849)

Typeset and illustrated by Tech-Set, Gateshead, Tyne and Wear

Contents

Preface

Essential Maths Book 7S has been written for pupils in Year 7 who are working towards or have attained National Curriculum Level 3. It is also designed for students who have only just succeeded at Level 4.

The material covers selected topics from the Secondary numeracy strategy Year 7 guide with Support material from the earlier Key Stage programmes. There is a comprehensive numeracy strategy guide at the start of the book with references to all topics.

There is no set path through the books but topics appear in the order suggested in the numeracy strategy planning charts. Broadly speaking, the book is split into 6 parts with a Review Section for use as revision or test material at the end of each half-term.

The authors recognise that there is a wealth of ideas available for 'starter' activities and many developing opportunities to explore mathematics through the use of ICT. The purpose of this book is to provide the main material for pupils to work at in a systematic way which helps to build up their confidence.

No textbook will have the 'right' amount of material for every class and the authors believe that it is better to have too much material rather than too little.

Each topic is broken down into two sections. Section M is the main activity and should be suitable for all children at this level. Section E is the extension work. Pupils may move naturally onto this work after Section M, or teachers will judge that a number of students should only tackle Section E.

Explanations are kept to a minimum because it is assumed that teachers will explore each topic fully in line with the NNS guidance.

The author is indebted to the contributions from Stephen Pearce and Peter Gibson.

Michael White

Support material

Numbers and the number system

Place value, ordering and rounding

10, 11
- Read and write whole numbers in figures and words, and know what each digit represents.

20
- **Multiply and divide any positive integer up to 10000 by 10 or 100 and understand the effect** (eg. $9900 \div 10$, $737 \div 10$, $2060 \div 100$).

84, 85
- Order a set of integers less than 1 million.

Properties of numbers and number sequences

2, 3, 124
- Recognise and extend number sequences formed by counting from any number is steps of constant size, extending beyond zero when counting back.

86, 87, 161
- Recognise multiples of 6, 7, 8, 9, up the 10th multiple. Know and apply tests of divisibility by 2, 4, 5, 10 or 100.

1
- Know squares of numbers to at least 10×10.

88, 89, 186, 187
- Find all the pairs of factors of any number to 100.

1
- Recognise and extend number sequences, such as the sequence of square numbers, or the sequence of triangular numbers 1, 3, 6, 10, 15, ...

6, 90
- Recognise prime numbers to at least 20.

Fractions, decimals and percentages, ratio and proportion

50, 51, 64, 151
- Use fraction notation, including mixed numbers, and the vocabulary 'numerator' and 'denominator.' Change an improper fraction to a mixed number (eg. change $\frac{13}{10}$ to $1\frac{3}{10}$).
  Recognise when two simple fractions are equivalent, including relating hundredths to tenths (eg. $\frac{70}{100} = \frac{7}{10}$).

152
- Order a set of fractions such as 2, $2\frac{3}{4}$, $1\frac{3}{4}$, $2\frac{1}{2}$, $1\frac{1}{2}$, and position them on a number line.

61, 144–146
- **Relate fractions to division.**

61, 147
- **Use a fraction as an 'operator' to find fractions, including tenths and hundredths, of numbers or quantities.**

150
- Solve simple problems using ideas of ratio and proportion ('one for every' and 'one in every ...').

58–60
- **Use decimal notation for tenths and hundredths.**
  Know what each digit represents in a number with up to two decimal places. Order a set of numbers or measurements with the same number of decimal places.

61, 148, 149
- **Relate fractions to their decimal** representations: that is, recognise the equivalence between the decimal and fraction forms of one half, one quarter, three quarters ... and tenths and hundredths (eg. $\frac{7}{10} = 0\cdot7$, $\frac{27}{100} = 0\cdot27$).

52–57, 135
- Begin to understand percentage as the number of parts in every 100, and find simple percentages of small whole-number quantities (eg. 25% of £8). Express one half, one quarter, three quarters, and tenths and hundredths, as percentages (eg. know that $\frac{3}{4} = 75\%$).

Calculations

Mental calculation strategies (+ and −)

83, 191
- Find differences by counting up through next multiple of 10, 100 or 1000, **eg. calculate mentally a difference such as 8006 − 2993.**

192
- Partition into H, T and U, adding the most significant digits first.

119
- Identify near doubles, such as $1\cdot5 + 1\cdot6$.

190, 192
- Add or subtract the nearest multiple of 10 or 100, then adjust.

7, 12, 13
- Use known number facts and place value for mental addition and subtraction (eg. $470 + 380$, $810 - 380$, $7\cdot4 + 9\cdot8$, $9\cdot2 - 8\cdot6$).

Understanding multiplication and division

100, 101
- Understand and use the relationships between the four operations, and the principles (not the names) of the arithmetic laws. Use brackets.

96, 97, 198, 199
- Round up or down after division, depending on the context.

Rapid recall of multiplication and division facts

8, 9, 81, 82, 188, 189
- Know by heart all multiplication facts up to 10×10.

Mental calculation strategies (× and ÷)

154, 155
- Use doubling or halving, starting from known facts. For example:
  – double/halve any two-digit number by doubling/halving the tens first.
  – double one number and halve the other.

156
- Partition (eg. $47 \times 6 = (40 \times 6) + (7 \times 6)$).

157
- Use the relationship between multiplication and division.

Pencil and paper procedures (× and ÷)

91–95
158–160
196, 197,
200
- **Written methods for:**
  – **short multiplication of HTU or U.t by U;**
  – **long multiplication of TU by TU;**
  – **short division of HTU by U** (with integer remainder);
  – **long multiplication of a three-digit by a two-digit integer;**
  – **short division of numbers involving decimals.**

Using a calculator

21
- Develop calculator skills and use a calculator effectively.

Solving Problems

Reasoning and generalising about numbers or shapes.

32, 80, 193, 206, 207
- Explain methods and reasoning, orally and in writing.

32, 40, 80, 169, 193, 206, 207, 222
- Solve mathematical problems or puzzles, recognise and explain patterns and relationships, generalise and predict.

Shape, space and measures

Measures

102, 103
- Use, read and write standard metric units (km, m, cm, mm, kg, g, l, ml), including their abbreviations, and relationships between them.

National Numeracy Strategy Guide

24, 104, 105
- Suggest suitable units and measuring equipment to estimate or measure lengths, mass or capacity. Measure and draw lines to the nearest millimetre. Record estimates and readings from scales to a suitable degree of accuracy.

26, 27
- **Understand area measured in square centimetres (cm²). Understand and use the formula in words 'length × breadth' for the area of a rectangle.** Understand, measure and calculate perimeters of rectangles and regular polygons.

107–112
- Use units of time. Use timetables.

Shape and space

68, 69
- Recognise properties of rectangles. Classify triangles (isosceles, equilateral, scalene), using criteria such as equal sides, equal angles, lines of symmetry.

30–33
- Make shapes with increasing accuracy. Visualise 3-D shapes from 2-D drawings and identify different nets for a closed cube.

134–137, 170–172
- Recognise reflection symmetry in regular polygons; for example, know that a square has four axes of symmetry and an equilateral triangle has three. Complete symmetrical patterns with two lines of symmetry at right angles (using squared paper or pegboard). Recognise where a shape will be after reflection in a mirror line parallel to one side (sides not all parallel or perpendicular to the mirror line). Recognise where a shape will be after translation.

70–72, 117–119
- Read and plot co-ordinates in the first quadrant.

73, 138–143
- Recognise and estimate angles. **Use a protractor to measure and draw acute and obtuse angles to the nearest degree.** Calculate angles in a straight line. Calculate angles in a triangle or around a point.

Handling data

Handling data

42, 43, 116–118, 120, 121, 176–178
- Solve a problem by representing, extracting and interpreting data in tables, graphs, charts and diagrams, including those generated by a computer, for example:
  - line graphs
  - frequency tables and bar charts with grouped discrete data.

Year 7 Material
Using and applying mathematics to solve problems

Applying mathematics and solving problems

22, 23, 113–115, 157
- **Solve word problems and investigate in** a range of contexts: number, algebra, shape, space and measures, and handling data.

120, 121, 184, 185
- Identify the necessary information to solve a problem; represent problems mathematically, making correct use of symbols, words, diagrams, tables and graphs.

Numbers and the number system

Place value, ordering and rounding

98, 99
- Round positive whole numbers to the nearest 10, 100 or 1000 and decimals to the nearest whole number.

Integers, powers and roots

14, 15
- Understand negative numbers as positions on a number line; order negative numbers.

122, 123
- Recognise the first few triangular numbers, squares of numbers to at least 12×12 and the corresponding roots.

Fractions, decimals, percentages, ratio and proportion

48, 49
- Use fraction notation to describe parts of shapes and to express a smaller whole number as a fraction of a larger one.

61, 147
- Calculate simple fractions of quantities and measurements (whole-number answers).

52–57, 62, 63, 148, 149, 208, 209, 209
- Understand percentage as the 'number of parts per 100'; **recognise the equivalence** of percentages, fractions and decimals; calculate simple percentages and use percentages to compare simple proportions.

Calculations

Number operations and the relationships between them

16, 17, 19, 20, 41, 156, 164, 196, 197, 210, 211
- Understand addition, subtraction, multiplication and division as they apply to whole numbers and decimals; know how to use the laws of arithmetic and inverse operations.

100, 101
- **Know and use the order of operations,** including brackets.

Mental methods and rapid recall of number facts

8, 9
- Consolidate the rapid recall of number facts, including positive integer complements to 100 and multiplication facts to 10×10, and quickly derive associated division facts.

62, 63
- Consolidate and **extend mental methods of calculation to include decimals, fractions and percentages,** accompanied where appropriate by suitable jottings; solve simple word problems mentally.

Written methods

16–20, 194, 195
- Use standard column procedures to add and subtract whole numbers and decimals with up to two places.

94
- **Multiply three-digit by two-digit whole numbers.**

Calculator methods

125, 201
- Carry out calculations with more than one step using brackets; use the square root key.

201
- Enter numbers and interpret the display in different contexts (decimals, money).

Algebra

Equations, formulae and identities

4, 5, 66, 67, 162, 163
- **Use letter symbols to represent unknown numbers or variables;** Know the meaning of the words *term*, *expression* and *equation*.

66, 67, 162, ● **Understand that algebraic operations**
163 **follow the same conventions and order**
as arithmetic operations

65, 165 ● Simplify linear algebraic expressions by
collecting like terms.

212–217 ● Construct and solve simple linear
equations with integer coefficients
(unknown on one side only) using
an appropriate method (e.g. inverse
operations).

218, 219 ● Substitute positive integers into simple
linear expressions.

Sequences, functions and graphs

1, 2, 3, 124, ● Generate and describe simple integer
sequences.

220–222 ● Generate sequences from practical
contexts and describe the general term in
simple cases.

Shape, space and measures

Geometrical reasoning: lines, angles and shapes

74, 75, 226, ● **Identify parallel and perpendicular lines:**
227 **know the sum of angles at a point, on a**
straight line and in a triangle.

32 ● Use 2-D representations to visualise 3-D
shapes.

Transformations

136, 137, ● Understand and use the language and
171, 172 notation associated with reflections,
translations and rotations.

173 ● Recognise rotational symmetry.

Coordinates

223–226 ● Use conventions and notation for 2-D
coordinates in all four quadrants.

Construction

24, 138–140 ● Use a ruler and protractor to:
– measure and draw lines to the nearest
millimetre and angles, including reflex
angles, to the nearest degree;

228–229 ● Use ruler and protractor to construct
simple nets of 3-D shapes, e.g. cuboid,
regular tetrahedron, square-based
pyramid, triangular prism.

Measures and mensuration

25, 105, 106 ● Use names and abbreviations of units of
measurement to measure, estimate,
calculate and solve problems in everyday
contexts involving length, area, mass,
capacity, time and angle;
convert one metric unit to another
(e.g. grams to kilograms); read and
interpret scales on a range of measuring
instruments.

138–140 ● Use angle measure; distinguish between
and estimate the size of acute, obtuse
and reflex angles.

28, 29 ● Know and use the formula for the area of
a rectangle; calculate the perimeter and
area of shapes made from rectangles.

Handling data

Specifying a problem, planning and collecting data

120, 121, ● Plan how to collect and organise small
184, 185 sets of data; design a data collection
sheet or questionnaire to use in a simple
survey; construct frequency tables for
discrete data, grouped where appropriate
in equal class intervals.

120, 121, ● Collect small sets of data from surveys.
184, 185

Processing and representing data, using ICT as appropriate

34, 35, 174, ● Calculate statistics for small sets of
175 discrete data:
– find the mode, median and range,
– calculate the mean.

Probability

44, 45 ● Use vocabulary and ideas of probability,
drawing on experience.

44–47, ● Understand and use the probability scale
179–181 from 0 to 1; find and justify probabilities
based on equally likely outcomes in
simple contexts.

182, 183 ● Collect data from a simple experiment
and record in a frequency table; estimate
probabilities based on this data.

Square Numbers

On this page you will learn to recognise square numbers.

M

Ask your teacher for cubes or cut out some small squares of equal size.

1. Using only 9 cubes, can you arrange them all to make one large square? Make a copy of this in your book.

2. Can you make one large square using exactly 16 cubes?

3. Can you make one large square using exactly 12 cubes?

4. Can you make one large square using exactly:
   a) 4 cubes
   b) 8 cubes
   c) 20 cubes
   d) 25 cubes
   e) 18 cubes?

   Talk to your teacher about your answers.

5. $1 = 1 \times 1 = 1^2$

    $4 = 2 \times 2 = 2^2$

   $9 = 3 \times 3 = 3^2$

   Using squared paper, continue this pattern up to 10^2.

E

1. $1^2 = 1 \qquad = 1$

   $2^2 = 1 + 3 \qquad = 4$

   $3^2 = 1 + 3 + 5 = 9$

   Continue this table up to 12^2.

2. Find the 2 missing numbers in each of these patterns:

   a) 1 4 9 16 ☐ 36 49 64 ☐ 100

   b) 4 7 10 ☐ 16 19 22 ☐ 28

   c) 1 6 11 16 21 ☐ 31 36 41 ☐

   d) 1 3 6 10 15 ☐ ☐

   e) 100 ☐ 64 49 36 ☐ 16 9 4 1

3. Look at this pattern:

Draw and continue this pattern up to 55. These numbers are called *TRIANGULAR NUMBERS*.

On these pages you will learn to extend number sequences.

To find the rule that links the numbers, look at the gaps.

Examples

2 4 6 8 10　　　　The rule is 'add 2'.

20 16 12 8 4　　　The rule is 'subtract 4'.

Ⓜ

Copy and complete by filling in the boxes.

① 16 18 20 22 ☐ ☐　　　　⑦ 17 22 27 32 ☐ ☐

② 9 12 15 18 ☐ ☐　　　　⑧ 4 7 10 13 ☐ ☐

③ 12 16 20 24 ☐ ☐　　　　⑨ 17 15 13 11 ☐ ☐

④ 5 10 15 20 ☐ ☐　　　　⑩ 28 23 18 13 ☐ ☐

⑤ 29 31 33 35 ☐ ☐　　　　⑪ 3 7 11 15 ☐ ☐

⑥ 22 18 14 10 ☐ ☐　　　　⑫ 24 21 18 15 ☐ ☐

Copy the sequences and write the next three numbers.

What is the rule for each sequence?

⑬ 17 19 21 23　　　　　　㉒ 97 93 89 85

⑭ 30 34 38 42　　　　　　㉓ 143 243 343 543

⑮ 9 14 19 24　　　　　　㉔ 58 55 52 49

⑯ 937 837 737 637　　　　㉕ 475 450 425 400

⑰ 51 49 47 45　　　　　　㉖ 141 130 119 108

⑱ 16 26 36 46　　　　　　㉗ 30 70 110 150

⑲ 52 47 42 37　　　　　　㉘ 57 63 69 75

⑳ 63 66 69 72　　　　　　㉙ 1 $1\frac{1}{2}$ 2 $2\frac{1}{2}$

㉑ 84 74 64 54　　　　　　㉚ 3·2 3·3 3·4 3·5

E

Write the first six numbers in each sequence.

	Start at	Rule			Start at	Rule
①	19	Add 3		⑦	20	Add 30
②	180	Subtract 20		⑧	70	Subtract 7
③	12	Add 6		⑨	70	Add 40
④	72	Subtract 9		⑩	30	Subtract 4
⑤	40	Add 8		⑪	25	Add 25
⑥	86	Subtract 11		⑫	325	Subtract 50

Questions ⑬ to ㉔ are sequences with negative numbers.
Copy and complete by filling in the boxes

⑬ ☐ ☐ −3 −2 ☐ 0 1 2 ☐ 4 5

⑭ −10 −8 ☐ −4 −2 ☐ 2 ☐ ☐ 8 10

⑮ 5 4 ☐ ☐ 1 0 ☐ ☐ −3 −4 −5

⑯ 10 8 6 4 2 0 −2 ☐ ☐ ☐ ☐

⑰ 3 2 ☐ ☐ ☐ −2 −3 ☐

⑱ ☐ ☐ ☐ 1 2 3 4 ☐

⑲ ☐ ☐ −4 −6 −8 −10 ☐ −14

⑳ −10 ☐ −8 ☐ −6 ☐ −4

㉑ −10 −8 ☐ −4 ☐ ☐ 2

㉒ −7 ☐ ☐ −1 1 3 5 ☐

㉓ 6 4 2 ☐ ☐ ☐ −6 ☐ ☐ −12

㉔ 5 ☐ 1 ☐ −3 ☐ −7 ☐ ☐ ☐

On these pages you will learn to use letters in place of numbers.

This menu is in a café.

c	coffee	75p
t	tea	65p
p	pepsi	85p
ℓ	lemonade	80p
s	soup	90p
r	roll	40p
b	burger	95p
i	ice-cream	75p

Tom, the waiter, cannot add up the money very quickly so he uses a code.

If somebody orders one soup and one roll, he writes s + r.

Later, he can work out the money because s + r means 90p + 40p = 130p or £1·30

THE LETTERS CAN BE USED IN PLACE OF THE NUMBERS.

If someone orders 3 soups, Tom writes 3s. Later, he works out the money as 3 × 90p because the order was 3 lots of soup.

This means 3s is 3 × s which is 3 × 90p = £2·70

If someone orders 2 coffees, 3 burgers and one ice-cream, Tom writes

$$2c + 3b + i$$

What would Tom write for each of the following orders:

1. 2 burgers and one pepsi.
2. 1 burger, 1 roll and 1 lemonade.
3. 2 soups, 2 rolls and 2 teas.
4. 3 coffees, 2 teas and 1 roll.
5. 1 soup, 2 rolls and 2 pepsis.
6. 1 lemonade, 2 coffees, 2 teas and 1 pepsi.
7. 3 soups, 2 rolls, 2 coffees and 2 teas.
8. Two burgers, three rolls and four lemonades.
9. Four burgers, three soups, 2 lemonades and one pepsi.
10. Two ice-creams, one soup, two pepsis and 1 tea.

For each order below, work out the cost in money.

(11) b + ℓ

(12) s + r + i

(13) s + i + c

(14) 2s

(15) 3ℓ

(16) 2s + r

(17) 2c + ℓ

(18) 2c + 2ℓ

(19) 2s + 2r + p

(20) 3s + r + 2i

Another café has this menu.

s	sausage	45p
c	chips	90p
f	fish	£1·70
b	burger	£1·15
a	apple pie	£1·10
t	tango	60p
ℓ	lucozade	75p

Using the code, what would be written down for each of the following orders:

(1) One fish and one chips.

(2) One chips, two sausages and one tango.

(3) Two chips, one burger, one sausage and two lucozades.

(4) Three sausages, one chips and two apple pies.

(5) Three apple pies, one tango and three lucozades.

(6) Three fish, four chips, two sausages and two apple pies.

For each order below, work out the cost in money.

(7) 2a + b + t

(8) 2f + 2c + 2ℓ

(9) 3f + 2c + 2i + t + ℓ

(10) 2b + c + 2t

(11) 2s + c + i + ℓ

(12) 3b + 4c + 3a + 2t + 2ℓ

On this page you will learn to recognise prime numbers.

> A prime number can only be divided exactly by two different numbers (These are the number 1 and itself).
>
> 5 is a prime number because $5 \div \underline{1} = 5$ and $5 \div \underline{5} = 1$ (5 can be divided by 1 and itself). You cannot find $5 \div \underline{2}$ or $5 \div \underline{3}$ or $5 \div \underline{4}$ without a remainder.
>
> Notice that 1 is NOT a prime number.

M

1. Which of these divisions have no remainder?

   a) $7 \div 1$ e) $7 \div 5$

   b) $7 \div 2$ f) $7 \div 6$

   c) $7 \div 3$ g) $7 \div 7$

   d) $7 \div 4$

   If only (a) and (g) have no remainder, 7 is a prime number (7 can only be divided exactly by 1 and itself).

2. Which of these divisions have no remainder?

   a) $6 \div 1$ d) $6 \div 4$

   b) $6 \div 2$ e) $6 \div 5$

   c) $6 \div 3$ f) $6 \div 6$

   Is 6 a prime number? (i.e. Can 6 only be divided exactly by 1 and itself?)

3. By dividing each of these numbers by the smaller numbers, write down whether they are prime or not:

   a) 4   e) 13

   b) 11   f) 3

   c) 8   g) 18

   d) 15   h) 19

E

1. Copy this grid and shade in all the boxes which have a prime number in them.

20	7	10	9
30	11	14	25
2	13	22	23
1	21	16	27

   When you have finished, add up all the numbers in the shaded boxes. The answer should be 56.

2. Write down the prime number in each group.

   a) 7, 8, 9

   b) 16, 17, 18

   c) 21, 22, 23

   d) 27, 28, 29

   e) 19, 20, 21

   f) 13, 14, 15

3. Find the next prime number after 30.

4. Find the next prime number after 40.

5. What is the largest two digit prime number?

On this page you will use a variety of strategies to add or subtract pairs of numbers mentally.

Copy and complete the squares.

(1)

+	8	9	6
9	17		
7			
8			

(3)

+	24	32	53
15			
43			96
34			

(5)

+	9	21	29
62			
35			
57			

(7)

+	34	75	93
200			
800			
500			

(2)

−	8	7	9
19	11		
16			
18			9

(4)

−	43	26	55
78		52	
67			
99			

(6)

−	11	19	21
48			
24			
76			

(8)

−	7	9	6
104			
503			
605			

Write the answers only.

(9) 1268 + 5

(10) 150 + 60

(11) 300 − 7

(12) 76 − 8

(13) 800 + 500

(14) 463 + 8

(15) 80 + 37

(16) 8000 − 6

(17) 85 − 30

(18) 300 + 257

(19) 48 + 23

(20) 74 − 27

(21) 70 + 50

(22) 53 + 40

(23) 405 − 9

(24) 5001 − 4993

Add 49 to:

(25) 50

(26) 23

(27) 47

Add 57 to:

(28) 48

(29) 300

(30) 230

Take 71 from:

(31) 95

(32) 143

(33) 118

Take 36 from:

(34) 63

(35) 81

(36) 55

Make 100.

(37) 43 + ☐

(38) 92 + ☐

(39) 14 + ☐

E

Copy and complete by writing the missing number in the box.

(1) 450 + ☐ = 730

(2) 720 − ☐ = 430

(3) 4005 − ☐ = 2993

(4) 8·3 − ☐ = 1·8

(5) ☐ + 190 = 550

(6) 985 − ☐ = 420

(7) ☐ − 800 = 561

(8) 6·2 + ☐ = 10·0

(9) 5002 − ☐ = 4899

(10) 567 + ☐ = 600

(11) 740 − ☐ = 280

(12) 4·2 + ☐ = 5

(13) 350 + ☐ = 510

(14) 1231 − ☐ = 700

(15) 329 + ☐ = 400

Addition and Multiplication Facts

On these pages you will practise using addition and multiplication.

Ⓜ **Part 1**

Copy and complete.

① $60 + \square = 120$

② $70 + \square = 150$

③ $\square + 60 = 140$

④ $\square + 70 = 160$

⑤ $80 + \square = 180$

⑥ $80 + \square = 130$

⑦ $\square + 90 = 150$

⑧ $\square + 80 = 150$

⑨ $80 + \square = 160$

⑩ $90 + \square = 180$

⑪ $\square + 70 = 140$

⑫ $\square + 90 = 170$

What do you need to add to each number to make 100?

⑬ 28   ⑲ 68

⑭ 63   ⑳ 75

⑮ 39   ㉑ 34

⑯ 83   ㉒ 79

⑰ 19   ㉓ 41

⑱ 46   ㉔ 57

What do you need to add to each number to make 1000?

㉕ 850   ㉛ 250

㉖ 550   ㉜ 450

㉗ 150   ㉝ 700

㉘ 300   ㉞ 50

㉙ 750   ㉟ 350

㉚ 950   ㊱ 650

Part 2

Write out the 6 times table. Use the table to work out:

① 5×6

② 2×6

③ 7×6

④ 4×6

⑤ 0×6

⑥ 6×6

⑦ 9×6

⑧ 1×6

⑨ 10×6

⑩ 8×6

⑪ $12 \div 6$

⑫ $48 \div 6$

⑬ $24 \div 6$

⑭ $36 \div 6$

⑮ $6 \div 6$

⑯ $42 \div 6$

⑰ $18 \div 6$

⑱ $60 \div 6$

⑲ $30 \div 6$

⑳ $54 \div 6$

㉑ 6×4

㉒ 6×1

㉓ 6×7

㉔ 6×2

㉕ 6×8

㉖ 6×3

㉗ 6×9

㉘ 6×0

㉙ 6×5

㉚ 6×10

Part 3

Write out the 9 times table. Use the table to work out:

① 3×9

② 10×9

③ 7×9

④ 1×9

⑤ 5×9

⑥ 2×9

⑦ 6×9

⑧ 9×9

⑨ 0×9

⑩ 8×9

⑪ $36 \div 9$

⑫ $63 \div 9$

⑬ $18 \div 9$

⑭ $45 \div 9$

⑮ $90 \div 9$

⑯ $9 \div 9$

⑰ $81 \div 9$

⑱ $27 \div 9$

⑲ $72 \div 9$

⑳ $54 \div 9$

㉑ 9×5

㉒ 9×2

㉓ 9×1

㉔ 9×7

㉕ 9×4

㉖ 9×0

㉗ 9×10

㉘ 9×3

㉙ 9×6

㉚ 9×8

E **Part 1**

Write out the 7 times table. Use the table to work out:

1. 3×7
2. 2×7
3. 5×7
4. 1×7
5. 8×7
6. 0×7
7. 7×7
8. 4×7
9. 9×7
10. 6×7

11. $28 \div 7$
12. $14 \div 7$
13. $70 \div 7$
14. $7 \div 7$
15. $42 \div 7$
16. $21 \div 7$
17. $63 \div 7$
18. $49 \div 7$
19. $35 \div 7$
20. $56 \div 7$

21. 7×7
22. 7×5
23. 7×9
24. 7×1
25. 7×3
26. 7×6
27. 7×0
28. 7×4
29. 7×10
30. 7×8

Part 2

Write out the 8 times table. Use the table to work out:

1. 5×8
2. 2×8
3. 10×8
4. 4×8
5. 9×8
6. 7×8
7. 1×8
8. 8×8
9. 0×8
10. 6×8

11. $24 \div 8$
12. $80 \div 8$
13. $64 \div 8$
14. $16 \div 8$
15. $48 \div 8$
16. $8 \div 8$
17. $40 \div 8$
18. $72 \div 8$
19. $32 \div 8$
20. $56 \div 8$

21. 8×3
22. 8×6
23. 8×2
24. 8×0
25. 8×10
26. 8×1
27. 8×4
28. 8×9
29. 8×5
30. 8×7

Part 3

Copy and complete:

1. $\boxed{} \times 9 = 27$
2. $\boxed{} \times 9 = 72$
3. $\boxed{} \times 9 = 45$
4. $\boxed{} \times 9 = 63$
5. $\boxed{} \div 9 = 4$
6. $\boxed{} \div 9 = 10$
7. $\boxed{} \div 9 = 8$
8. $\boxed{} \div 9 = 3$

9. $\boxed{} \times 6 = 0$
10. $\boxed{} \times 6 = 48$
11. $\boxed{} \times 6 = 30$
12. $\boxed{} \times 6 = 54$
13. $\boxed{} \div 6 = 5$
14. $\boxed{} \div 6 = 8$
15. $\boxed{} \div 6 = 10$
16. $\boxed{} \div 6 = 4$

17. A multi storey car park has 9 levels. There are 8 parking spaces on each level. How many cars can park in the car park?

18. Eggs are packed into boxes of 6. How many boxes are needed for 54 eggs?

On these pages you will read and write numbers in words.

You will need to know and use these words:

1 one	8 eight	15 fifteen	30 thirty
2 two	9 nine	16 sixteen	40 forty
3 three	10 ten	17 seventeen	50 fifty
4 four	11 eleven	18 eighteen	60 sixty
5 five	12 twelve	19 nineteen	70 seventy
6 six	13 thirteen	20 twenty	80 eighty
7 seven	14 fourteen	21 twenty-one	90 ninety

The way we read a digit depends upon its position in the number.

Examples

27 reads `twenty-seven'

274 reads `two hundred and seventy-four'

2745 reads `two thousand seven hundred and forty-five'

Ⓜ **Part 1**

The children in Class 7A have been writing their addresses.
Write these house numbers in figures.

① Chris   – thirteen
② Matthew – sixteen
③ Sarah   – forty-nine
④ Claire   – seventy-two
⑤ David   – three hundred

⑥ Emma – twelve
⑦ Laura – fifteen
⑧ Daniel – fifty-eight
⑨ Andy   – thirty-seven
⑩ Becky – ninety

Write each of these children's house numbers in words.

⑪ Gemma
⑭

⑮ Simon
㊀60

⑲ Katie
500

⑫ Rachel
18

⑯ Michael
17

⑳ Ryan
1000

⑬ Kelly
26

⑰ Vicky
19

㉑ Jenny
32

⑭ Andrew
95

⑱ Mark
83

㉒ Marcus
200

Part 2

Write the numbers of these raffle tickets in words.

① 43 ③ 176 ⑤ 238 ⑦ 424 ⑨ 317

② 789 ④ 52 ⑥ 540 ⑧ 635 ⑩ 861

The prize winning numbers were called out. Draw the tickets.

⑪ Sixty-five.

⑫ One hundred and forty-two.

⑬ Five hundred and ninety-four.

⑭ Four hundred and sixty.

⑮ Seventy-seven.

⑯ Two hundred and fifty-one.

⑰ Eight hundred and twelve.

⑱ Six hundred and nine.

⑲ One hundred and eighty.

⑳ Nine hundred and eighty-four.

E

Write the heights of these mountains in words.

① Everest   8848 m

② Ben Nevis   1343 m

③ Sca Fell   978 m

④ Elbrus   5033 m

⑤ Etna   3340 m

⑥ Mt. McKinley 6195 m

⑦ Snowdon   1085 m

⑧ Mont Blanc   4807 m

⑨ Kilimanjaro   5895 m

⑩ Annapurna   8078m

⑪ Use these digits.

3 1 7 0

Make as many four-digit numbers as you can with a value of less than 2000.
There are six. Can you find them all?
Write the numbers:

a) in figures   b) in words.

⑫ Write these numbers in words.

a) 2003   b) 2030   c) 2300   d) 2303   e) 2330

On this page you will practise the vocabulary of addition and subtraction.

Ⓜ

Copy and complete.

1. The total of 43 and 18 is ☐.
2. 70 plus ☐ equals 114.
3. ☐ add 25 equals 100.
4. The sum of 52 and ☐ is 79.
5. 16 and 16 altogether is ☐.
6. Add ☐ to 97 to make 107.
7. 74 plus 19 equals ☐.
8. ☐ add 400 equals 1000.
9. Add 61 to ☐ to make 361.
10. The total of 46 and 35 is ☐.
11. The sum of 21 and ☐ is 59.
12. ☐ and 400 altogether is 1200.

Work out:

13. Take 100 from 214.
14. 21 less than 47.
15. 502 subtract 8.
16. 36 less than 89.
17. 115 take away 40.
18. Subtract 6 from 74.

Copy and complete.

19. $400 - ☐ = 330$
20. $☐ - 19 = 53$
21. $1002 - ☐ = 9$
22. $☐ - 600 = 700$
23. $257 - ☐ = 247$
24. $☐ - 45 = 100$
25. $743 - ☐ = 743$
26. $☐ - 31 = 27$

Ⓔ

Copy and complete.

1. $68 + ☐ = 100$
2. $160 + ☐ = 196$
3. $☐ + 16 = 300$
4. $☐ + 61 = 127$
5. $158 + ☐ = 165$
6. $232 + ☐ = 272$
7. $☐ + 49 = 124$
8. $☐ + 43 = 283$
9. $257 + ☐ = 300$
10. $76 + ☐ = 134$
11. $☐ + 800 = 2000$
12. $☐ + 37 = 100$

13. A circus clown is fired 29 m on Monday and 36 m on Tuesday. How far is he fired altogether?

Find the difference between each pair of numbers.

14. 178   31
15. 6001   14
16. 28   75
17. 254   69
18. 230   160
19. 282   60
20. 1700   800
21. 83   57

On this page you will practise adding or subtracting multiples of 10 and 100.

M

Add 10

1. 327
2. 99
3. 464
4. 195.

Take 10

5. 142
6. 208
7. 576
8. 603.

Add 60

9. 40
10. 81
11. 70
12. 67.

Take 80

13. 155
14. 140
15. 126
16. 130.

Add 90

17. 60
18. 38
19. 80
20. 23.

Take 70

21. 119
22. 160
23. 132
24. 120.

Copy and complete:

25. 170 + ☐ = 200
26. 456 + ☐ = 556
27. 325 − ☐ = 225
28. 340 + ☐ = 400

29. 283 + ☐ = 383
30. 749 − ☐ = 649
31. 400 + ☐ = 1100
32. 290 + ☐ = 300

33. 1200 − ☐ = 400
34. 520 + ☐ = 600
35. 800 + ☐ = 1300
36. 1600 − ☐ = 700.

E

Add 60

1. 278
2. 381
3. 455
4. 763.

Take 70

13. 435
14. 629
15. 712
16. 556.

Add 70

5. 294
6. 546
7. 482
8. 679.

Take 80

17. 367
18. 943
19. 779
20. 434.

Add 80

9. 357
10. 894
11. 238
12. 561.

Take 90

21. 251
22. 886
23. 622
24. 548.

Copy and complete:

25. 247 + ☐ = 300
26. 1600 + ☐ = 2000
27. 336 + ☐ = 400
28. 3200 + ☐ = 4000

29. 472 + ☐ = 500
30. 2300 + ☐ = 3000
31. 753 + ☐ = 800
32. 5400 + ☐ = 6000

33. 584 + ☐ = 600
34. 7800 + ☐ = 8000
35. 818 + ☐ = 900
36. 8100 + ☐ = 9000.

On these pages you will learn to recognise and order negative numbers.

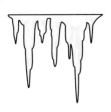 Negative numbers
Below zero
Have a minus sign

 Positive numbers
Above zero

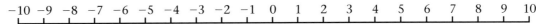

−10 −9 −8 −7 −6 −5 −4 −3 −2 −1 0 1 2 3 4 5 6 7 8 9 10

We often use negative numbers with temperatures.

$\mathbb{M}$

(1) What temperatures are shown by the letters?

(2) Which letter shows the coldest temperature?

(3) Give the difference in temperature between
   a) A and B
   b) A and C
   c) B and C.

(4) What would the temperature be if it was:
   a) at A and fell 7°
   b) at B and rose 9°

Find the difference between each pair of numbers.

(5) −6 −4   (7) −3 5   (9) −4 2   (11) 0 −4

(6) −2 2   (8) −1 3   (10) −1 −7   (12) 2 −3

Put these numbers in order, smallest first.

(13)
| −3 | 0 | −1 |
| 2 | 5 | |

(14)
| 4 | −3 |
| −1 | −5 | 1 |

(15)
| 3 | 0 | −4 |
| −2 | 1 | |

(16)
| 2 | −4 |
| 4 | −1 | 0 |

Copy and complete these tables showing changes in temperature.

(17)
Monday	Change	Tuesday
3°C	−4°C	−1°C
−1°C	+3°C	
0°C	−5°C	
4°C	−7°C	
−6°C	+2°C	
−2°C	+4°C	

(18)
Monday	Change	Tuesday
7°C	−4°C	3°C
−2°C		3°C
−4°C		−1°C
1°C		−3°C
0°C		−6°C
−3°C		4°C

E

Put each set of numbers in order, smallest first.

①
$$7 \quad -3$$
$$-6 \qquad 9$$
$$3 \quad -1$$

②
$$9 \quad -2$$
$$-8 \qquad 1$$
$$4 \quad 0$$

③
$$1 \quad -4$$
$$-7 \qquad 6$$
$$-1 \quad 2$$

④
$$-2 \quad 0$$
$$5 \qquad 3$$
$$-3 \quad -6$$

Look at the scale.

⑤ What temperatures are shown by the letters?

⑥ Which letter shows the coldest temperature?

⑦ Give the difference in temperature between:
   a) A and B   **b)** A and C   **c)** B and C.

⑧ What would the temperature be:
   a) if it was at A and fell 14°C?
   b) if it was at B and rose 18°C?
   c) if it was at C and fell 17°C?

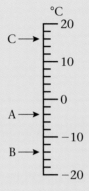

Look at the scale.

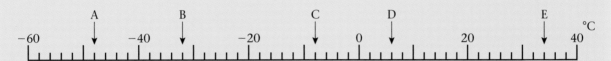

⑨ What temperatures are shown by the letters?

⑩ Give the difference in temperature between:
   a) C and D   **c)** C and E
   b) B and C   **d)** A and D.

⑪ What would the temperature be if it was:
   a) at A and rose 34°C?   **c)** at C and fell 26°C?
   b) at D and fell 18°C?   **d)** at B and rose 48°C?

Copy and complete the tables showing changes in temperature.

⑫

Old	Change	New
−4°C	+8°C	4°C
6°C	−11°C	
−23°C	+17°C	
12°C	−15°C	
−10°C	+9°C	
7°C	−20°C	

⑬

Old	Change	New
2°C	−5°C	−3°C
	+7°C	2°C
	+6°C	−5°C
	−11°C	−1°C
	+15°C	10°C
	−10°C	−14°C

⑭

Old	Change	New
7°C		−3°C
−5°C		−19°C
−2°C		14°C
3°C		−6°C
0°C		−17°C
8°C		−1°C

On these pages you will add and subtract whole numbers.

> **Examples**
> Line up units with units
> Line up tens with tens
>
> ```
>     3 8              3 2 6          ⁵6̸ ¹3        ⁷8̸ ¹4
>   + 4 4          +     4 5        − 2 7        − 2 5
>     8 2              3 7 1          3 6          5 9
>     1                    1
> ```

Ⓜ Part 1

Copy and complete

①   35
   + 28

②   46
   + 27

③   48
   + 36

④   57
   + 37

⑤   49
   + 39

⑥   66
   + 45

⑦   58
   + 54

⑧   89
   + 35

⑨   74
   + 68

⑩   97
   + 84

⑪   168
   + 57

⑫   185
   + 67

⑬   276
   + 59

⑭   237
   + 93

Part 2

Copy and complete.

①   72
   − 28

②   85
   − 38

③   64
   − 49

④   97
   − 58

⑤   73
   − 45

⑥   81
   − 37

⑦   62
   − 24

⑧   94
   − 55

⑨   63
   − 38

⑩   76
   − 57

⑪   55
   − 29

⑫   91
   − 48

⑬   82
   − 65

⑭   87
   − 59

E Part 1

Set out as in the examples on page 16.

1. 164 + 47
2. 179 + 59
3. 286 + 28
4. 348 + 79
5. 297 + 38

6. 296 + 46
7. 376 + 69
8. 468 + 86
9. 295 + 48
10. 589 + 77

11. Sanjay buys a computer for £475 and a printer for £89. How much does he spend altogether?

Work out

12. 64 + 19 + 225
13. 125 + 38 + 63
14. 327 + 141 + 44
15. 605 + 8 + 63
16. Copy and complete the addition square.

+	8			
12	20			
7		30		
		25		18
	16		9	

Part 2

Find the difference between each pair of numbers. Set out as in the examples.

1. 482 and 36
2. 245 and 29
3. 366 and 37
4. 173 and 68

5. 259 and 73
6. 317 and 75
7. 549 and 84
8. 428 and 91

9. 391 and 56
10. 264 and 38
11. 37 and 255
12. 45 and 372

13. 62 and 127
14. 36 and 463
15. 81 and 335
16. 594 and 55

17. Mike has 157 plates to be washed. So far he has washed 28. How many more plates does he have to wash?

18. A monster bouncy castle can hold a maximum of 1000 children. There are 227 children bouncing around inside.
How many fewer than the maximum is this?

On these pages you will learn to add and subtract with money.

Examples
Add £1·79 and 65p.
Line up the   £1·79
decimal points.   + £0·65
                              ─────
                               £2·44
                               ─────
                               1 1

Examples
Subtract £2·28 from £4·45.
Line up the   4·³4¹5
decimal points.   − 2· 2 8
                              ─────
                              2· 1 7

Ⓜ **Part 1**

Copy and complete.

①   £3·75   ④   £6·17
     + £0·43   + £0·93

②   £2·48   ⑤   £8·26
     + £0·09   + £0·77

③   £4·53   ⑥   £5·49
     + £1·08   + £0·84

⑦ Rhys bought a book for £3·49.
He had £0·68 left. How much
money did he have before he
bought the book?

Work out.

⑧ £2·48 + 37p

⑨ £3·65 + 94p + 31p

⑩ £5·76 + 85p + 13p

⑪ £2·54 + £1·38 + 99p

⑫ £3·62 + 51p + 64p

⑬ £3·58 + 37p + 29p

⑭ £4·67 + £2·13 + 9p

⑮ £6·23 + 46p + 8p

⑯ £8·45 + 72p + 6p

⑰ £7·60 + £1·18 + 34p

Part 2

Set out correctly and find the differences.

① 156 and 73   ⑦ £2·72 − £1·38

② 69 and 248   ⑧ £4·61 − £2·57

③ 377 and 95   ⑨ £5·80 − £2·34

④ 136 and 87   ⑩ £3·35 − £1·69

⑤ 74 and 456   ⑪ £6·27 − £3·43

⑥ 319 and 36   ⑫ £5·53 − £3·78

⑬ There were 256 people on a plane.
Of these 88 were men.
How many women were on the plane?

⑭ Liam has £7·29 in his piggy bank.
He takes out £1·40.
How much money is left in the piggy
bank?

E Part 1

Set out correctly and find the differences.

1. 1306 and 123
2. 198 and 2451
3. 4623 and 59
4. 473 and 3510
5. 5732 and 146
6. 88 and 6145

Work out

7. £3·35 − £1·79
8. £5·70 − £2·84
9. £4·21 − £2·53
10. £6·13 − £3·17
11. £8·42 − £7·50
12. £7·50 − £2·92

13. An ice cream seller has takings of £1321 on Saturday and £548 on Sunday. What is the difference in the takings?

14. Olivia has £7·17 in her purse. She spends £3·49. How much money is left in the purse?

15. On Monday Joe weighed 66 kg. By Friday he had lost 3·4 kg. How much did he weigh on Friday?

Part 2

Work out.

1. 5 + 0·26
2. 2·9 + 4·37
3. 8·62 + 7·99
4. 0·078 + 2·05

5. 10·04 + 3·005
6. 13·47 + 27·084
7. 1·97 + 19·7
8. 4·56 + 7·890

9. 456·7 + 8·901
10. 16·374 + 0·947 + 27
11. 3·142 + 2·71 + 8
12. 0·03 + 11 + 8·74

13. 29·6 − 14
14. 59·2 − 34·8
15. 81·8 − 29·9

16. Hassan bought a football costing £16·49 and paid with a £20 note. How much change did he get?

Work out.

17. 6·7 − 4·29
18. 47·2 − 27·42
19. 94·63 − 5·9
20. 2·97 − 1·414
21. 25·52 − 1·436
22. 3·142 − 1·414

On this page you will learn to multiply or divide by 1, 10 or 100.

Examples

$4 \times 1 = 4$ $4 \times 10 = 40$ $4 \times 100 = 400$

$400 \div 1 = 400$ $400 \div 10 = 40$ $400 \div 100 = 4$

M

Write the answers only.

1. 5×1
2. 2×10
3. 1×100
4. $800 \div 10$
5. $600 \div 100$

6. 6×10
7. $4 \div 1$
8. 5×100
9. $60 \div 10$
10. 9×1

Copy and complete.

11. $9 \times \square = 900$
12. $4 \times \square = 4$
13. $7 \times \square = 70$
14. $\square \times 1 = 3$
15. $\square \times 100 = 800$
16. $\square \times 10 = 40$
17. $1000 \div \square = 10$
18. $80 \div \square = 8$
19. $9 \div \square = 9$
20. $\square \div 10 = 50$
21. $\square \div 1 = 6$
22. $\square \div 100 = 7$
23. $10 \times \square = 100$
24. $\square \div 1 = 14$
25. $11 \times 100 = \square$

E

Write the answers only.

1. 14×10
2. 19×1
3. 25×100
4. $13 \div 1$
5. $240 \div 10$

6. $4200 \div 100$
7. 36×1
8. 52×100
9. $1800 \div 100$
10. $270 \div 10$

Copy and complete.

11. $24 \times \square = 2400$
12. $56 \times \square = 56$
13. $63 \times \square = 630$
14. $93 \div \square = 93$
15. $5200 \div \square = 52$
16. $670 \div \square = 67$
17. $\square \times 1 = 82$
18. $\square \times 100 = 1400$
19. $\square \times 10 = 390$
20. $\square \div 100 = 38$
21. $\square \div 1 = 45$
22. $\square \div 10 = 780$
23. $100 \times \square = 1000$
24. $\square \div 10 = 41$
25. $35 \times \square = 35000$

On this page you will learn:

- to recognise a negative number output.

Example 5 − 8

Press $\boxed{C}\boxed{5}\boxed{-}\boxed{8}\boxed{=}$ → −3

- to key in and interpret money calculations.

Example £3·12 × 5

Press $\boxed{C}\boxed{3}\boxed{\cdot}\boxed{1}\boxed{2}\boxed{\times}\boxed{5}\boxed{=}$ → 15·6   Answer = £15·60

Ⓜ

Use a calculator to work out the problems and interpret the display.

(1) 6 − 11   (6) 5 − 26
(2) 59 − 17   (7) 91 − 30
(3) 4 − 19   (8) 10 − 32
(4) 107 − 23   (9) £2·60 + 84p
(5) 3 − 16   (10) £3·90 + 67p

Now do these.

(11) £8·30 − 65p   (16) £9·17 − £2·77
(12) £6·07 − 49p   (17) 89 + (19 × 7)
(13) £2·52 + £3·78   (18) 9 × (93 − 46)
(14) £12·64 − £1·94   (19) 5 × (282 ÷ 6)
(15) £4·63 + £2·87   (20) 4 × (333 ÷ 9)

(21) There are 926 palm trees on an island. 53 are blown down in a hurricane. How many trees are left standing?

Ⓔ

Copy and complete.

(1) 86 + ☐ = 175
(2) ☐ + 59 = 243
(3) 165 + ☐ = 218
(4) ☐ + 67 = 123

(5) 135 − ☐ = 57
(6) ☐ − 86 = 161
(7) 253 − ☐ = 175
(8) ☐ − 127 = 248

(9) 318 − ☐ = 149
(10) ☐ + 137 = 283
(11) 712 − ☐ = 464
(12) ☐ − 254 = 379

(13) Find pairs of consecutive numbers which add up to:
  a) 65   c) 211
  b) 143   d) 275.

(14) The temperature is 14°C. It falls 36°C. What is the new temperature?

On these pages you will learn to use the vocabulary of multiplication.

Ⓜ Part 1
Write a number sentence for each problem and work out the answer.

① Multiply 3 by 8.

② What is 5 times 100?

③ What is 21 multiplied by 2?

④ Find 3 lots of 40.

⑤ Find the product of 7 and 3.

⑥ What is 9 times greater than 4?

⑦ Rosie has 6 pens. Luke has three times as many. How many pens does Luke have?

⑧ A tree is 8 times taller than a fence. The fence is 2m tall. How tall is the tree?

⑨ There are 6 eggs in a box. There are 5 boxes. How many eggs are there?

⑩ There are 12 cubes in a block. There are 3 blocks. How many cubes are there?

⑪ There are 9 spiders in a shed and each spider caught 8 flies. How many flies were caught altogether?

Part 2
Write a number sentence for each problem and work out the answer.

① Share 18 by 2.

② Divide 70 by 10.

③ What is 45 divided by 5?

④ How many 2s make 14?

⑤ Share 20 by 5.

⑥ Divide 20 by 2.

⑦ What is 50 divided by 10?

⑧ How many 5s make 35?

⑨ Five children share 40 sweets equally between them. How many sweets does each child have?

⑩ There are 30 children in a class. Half the children have a skateboard. How many children do not have a skateboard?

⑪ Six people win a prize of £540 between them. How much does each person get?

E

1 Look at the numbers in the box.

| 3 | 8 | 15 | 20 | 24 |

a What is the smallest number times the largest number?

b Multiply the middle number by the second largest.

c What is the second smallest number multiplied by itself?

d Which number is five times greater than the smallest number?

e Which number is three lots of the second smallest number?

f The product of two numbers in the box is equal to another number in the box. Find the three numbers.

g Ten different products can be made using pairs of the five numbers. Can you find them all?

2 A model of Stonehenge contains 36 rocks. How many rocks are there in 8 models?

3 A bus has 42 seats. How many passengers can be carried by a fleet of 7 buses?

4 There are 80 tea bags per packet of tea. How many tea bags are there altogether in nine packets?

Write a number sentence for each problem and work out the answer.

5 How many teams of 4 can be made from 32 children?

6 90 cm of string is cut into 3 equal lengths. How long is each length?

7 5 people win a competition. They share the £1000 prize between them. How much should each person get?

8 There were 24 boats in a race. 1 in every 3 of the boats sank. How many boats sank?

9 There are 24 children in a class.
a) 1 in every 2 children is a boy. How many boys are there?
b) 1 in every 3 has fair hair. How many children have fair hair?
c) 1 in every 4 has green eyes. How many children have green eyes?

10 Five people can travel in one car and there are altogether 80 people to transport. How many cars are needed?

On this page you will learn to use a ruler to measure length.

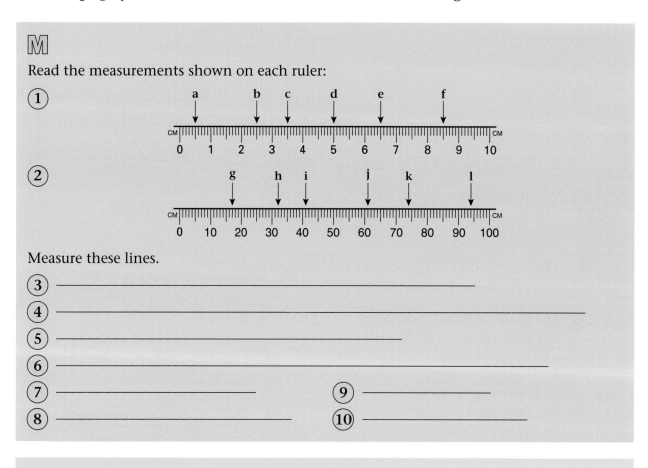

M

Read the measurements shown on each ruler:

1

2

Measure these lines.

3

4

5

6

7   9

8   10

E

1   Read the measurements shown to the nearest tenth of a centimetre.

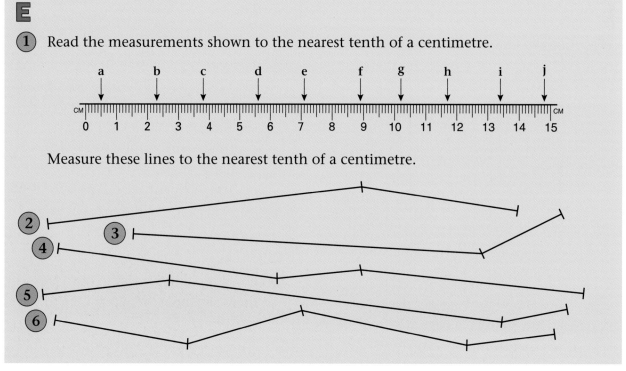

Measure these lines to the nearest tenth of a centimetre.

2

3

4

5

6

On this page you will learn to use the relationship between metric units of length and to suggest suitable units to measure lengths.

M

Make 1 metre.

1. 35 cm + ☐
2. 75 cm + ☐
3. ☐ + 15 cm
4. ☐ + 55 cm

Make 1 kilometre.

5. 200 m + ☐
6. 600 m + ☐
7. ☐ + 300 m
8. ☐ + 900 m

Suggest a suitable metric unit to measure the length of:

9. a shoe

10. a classroom
11. a running track
12. a car journey
13. a banana
14. a house
15. Africa
16. the distance to the Moon.

E

Copy and complete by writing the missing number in the box.

1. $\frac{1}{2}$ km = ☐ m
2. 3 km = ☐ m
3. 2 km = ☐ m
4. 5000 m = ☐ km
5. 3500 m = ☐ km
6. 4500 m = ☐ km
7. $\frac{1}{2}$ m = ☐ cm
8. 2 m = ☐ cm
9. 6 m = ☐ cm
10. 400 cm = ☐ m
11. 350 cm = ☐ m
12. 800 cm = ☐ m

Suggest a suitable metric unit to measure these lengths.

13. a finger
14. the height of a tree
15. the length of England
16. a woodpecker

17. the length of the classroom
18. an apple pip

Think of two more things you would measure using:

19. centimetres
20. metres.

Choose the longest length from each pair.

21. 500 m   5 km
22. 20 cm $\frac{1}{2}$ m
23. 40 cm $\frac{1}{4}$ m
24. $\frac{1}{2}$ km   400 m
25. 200 cm   1 m
26. 400 m   4 km

On this page you will learn how to measure and calculate the perimeter of a rectangle and other shapes.

Measure each side of each shape and work out the perimeter.

①    ② 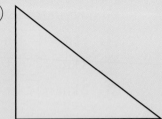   ③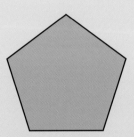

④ Work out the perimeters of these shapes.
  a) square sides – 7 cm   c) equilateral triangle – sides 6 cm
  b) rectangle sides – 8 cm 4 cm d) regular pentagon – sides 4 cm

⑤ Use squared paper. Draw a square with an area of 25cm². Work out the perimeter.

Work out the perimeters of these shapes.

⑥ rectangle – sides 5 cm 12 cm   ⑧ square – sides 4·5 cm

⑦ regular hexagon – sides 7 cm   ⑨ regular octagon – sides 9 cm

E

① Copy and complete this table showing the measurements of rectangles.

Length	8 cm	6 cm	7 cm		15 cm	
Width	4 cm			7 cm		5 cm
Perimeter		18 cm		34 cm	48 cm	

The lengths of these shapes are in cm. For each shape work out the perimeter.

② 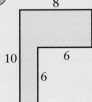   ③ 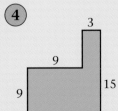   ④ 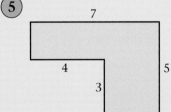   ⑤

On this page you will learn to calculate the areas of shapes by counting squares.

> The area of a shape is the amount of surface it covers.
>
> Area is measured in squares, usually square centimetres (cm²) or square metres (m²).
>
> **Example**   Area of rectangle = 24 cm²
>
>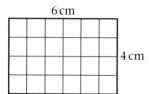
> 6 cm
> 4 cm

M

Find the area of each rectangle.

①  3 cm
5 cm

② 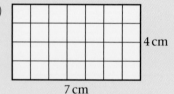 4 cm
7 cm

③ 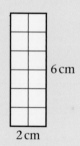 6 cm
2 cm

④ Draw a square with sides of 8 cm. Find its area.

⑤ Draw a square with an area of 16 cm². Work out the perimeter.

⑥ Draw a rectangle with an area of 15 cm² and a length of 5 cm. Work out the perimeter.

E

① Work out the areas of these letters by counting squares and half squares.

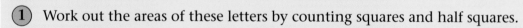

② Make up your own drawings of letters using squared paper. You could draw your initials. Work out the areas.

On these pages you will learn how to measure and calculate the area and perimeter of a rectangle and other shapes.

The area of a shape is the amount of surface it covers.

It is measured in squares, usually square metres (m^2) or square centimetres (cm^2).

The perimeter of a shape is the distance around its edges.

It is a length and is measured in units of length such as metres or centimetres.

To understand the difference between area and perimeter think of a field.
The perimeter is the fence. The area is the field itself.

Example

6 cm

4 cm

Area = length × breadth (l × b)

= (6 × 4) cm² = 24 cm²

Perimeter = 6 + 4 + 6 + 4

= 20 cm

Ⓜ

① Calculate the area of each rectangle. All lengths are in cm.

a)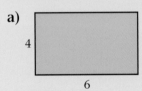
4
6

b)
3
7

c)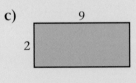
9
2

d)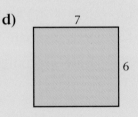
7
6

② Calculate the perimeter of each rectangle in Question ① above.

③ Use 1 cm² squared paper. Draw three different rectangles each with an area of 36 cm². Work out the perimeters.

④ Use 1 cm² squared paper. Draw three different rectangles each with a perimeter of 36 cm. Work out the areas.

⑤ Copy and complete this table showing the measurements of rectangles.

Length	9 cm	8 cm	6 cm	12 cm	6 cm	8 cm
Breadth	7 cm	3 cm				
Perimeter					26 cm	34 cm
Area			12 cm²	60 cm²		

Find the areas of the following irregular shapes. Each square represents 1 cm².

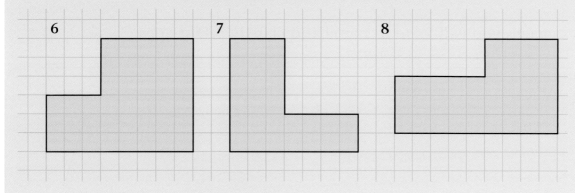

E

The lengths of these shapes are in cm. For each shape work out:

a) the area **b)** the perimeter.

①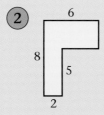

②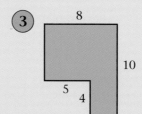

③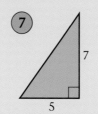

④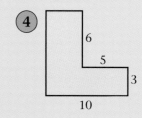

Use squared paper to draw the triangles.
Work out the area of each triangle

⑤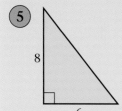

⑥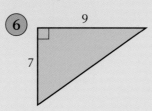

⑦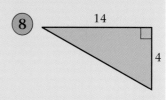

⑧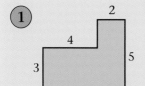

Work out the area of each triangle. All the lengths are in cm.

⑨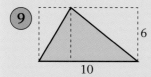

⑩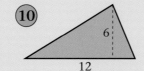

⑪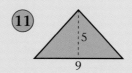

⑫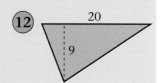

On these pages you will learn to name and classify 3-D shapes.

Some 3-D shapes with curved faces.

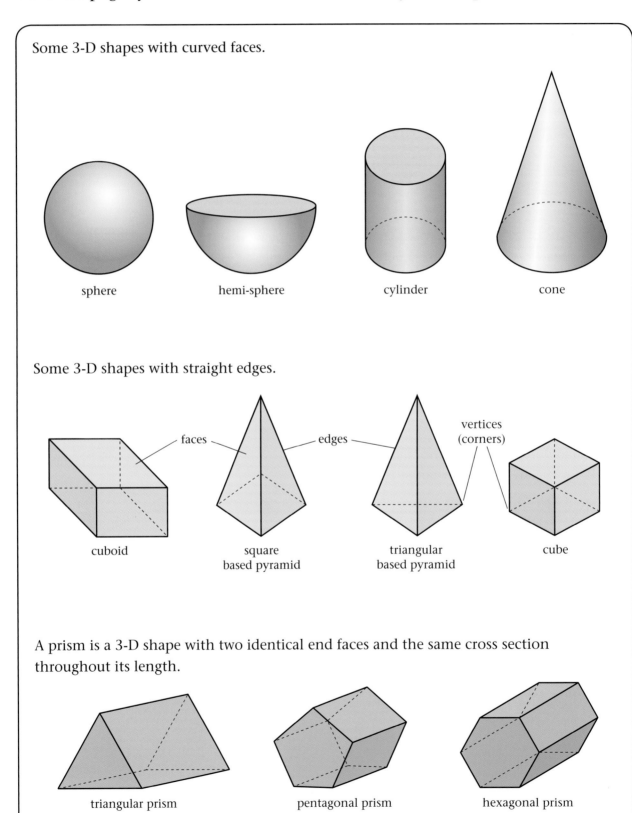

sphere   hemi-sphere   cylinder   cone

Some 3-D shapes with straight edges.

cuboid   square
based pyramid   triangular
based pyramid   cube

faces   edges   vertices
(corners)

A prism is a 3-D shape with two identical end faces and the same cross section throughout its length.

triangular prism   pentagonal prism   hexagonal prism

Here are some shapes.

①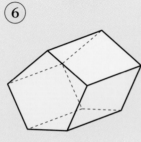

②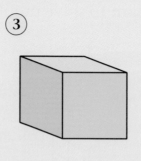

③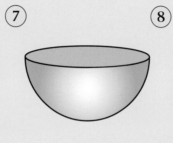

④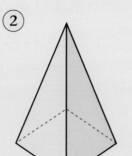

⑤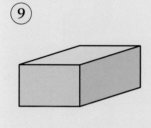

⑥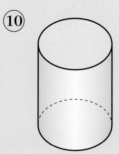

⑦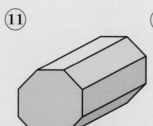

⑧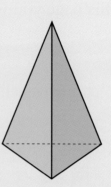

⑨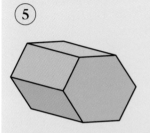

⑩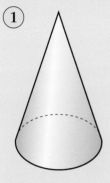

⑪

⑫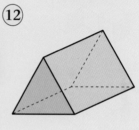

A

Write the name of each of the shapes.

B

Write the names of

① 4 shapes with curved faces

② 2 shapes with 8 vertices

③ 1 shape with 10 vertices

④ 2 shapes with 5 flat faces

⑤ 2 shapes with 1 circular flat face

⑥ 1 shape with 8 faces

⑦ 1 shape with 6 edges

⑧ 1 shape with 24 edges.

E

Copy and complete the table for each of the shapes.

No.	Shape	Flat faces	Edges	Vertices
1	cone	2	1	1
2	hexagonal prism	8	18	12

On this page you will learn to solve problems with 3-D shapes.

M

Use cubes to build these shapes.

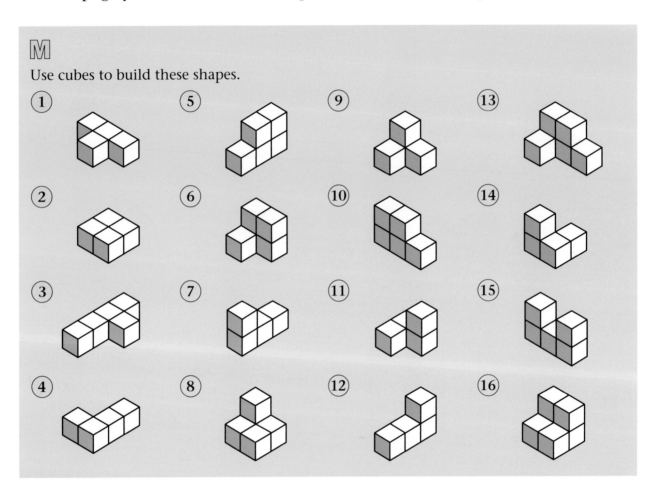

① 　　　 ⑤ 　　　 ⑨ 　　　 ⑬

② 　　　 ⑥ 　　　 ⑩ 　　　 ⑭

③ 　　　 ⑦ 　　　 ⑪ 　　　 ⑮

④ 　　　 ⑧ 　　　 ⑫ 　　　 ⑯

E

① Without using cubes, work out how many cubes are needed to build each shape above.

Example

6 cubes are needed.
(Only 5 cubes can be seen.)

② How many more cubes are needed to turn each shape into a cuboid?

Example

2 cubes are needed.

Check your answer by using cubes.

On this page you will learn to make nets for 3-D shapes.

M

① Copy these nets onto squared paper. Draw flaps as in the first diagram.
Cut them out and fold them to make open cubes.

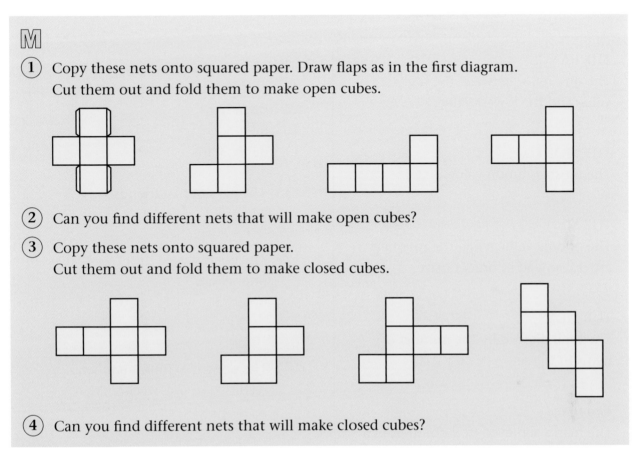

② Can you find different nets that will make open cubes?

③ Copy these nets onto squared paper.
Cut them out and fold them to make closed cubes.

④ Can you find different nets that will make closed cubes?

E

① Copy this net onto squared paper.
Remember to draw flaps.
Cut it out and fold it to make a
cuboid.

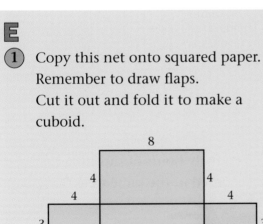

② Make nets for these cuboids.

a)

b)

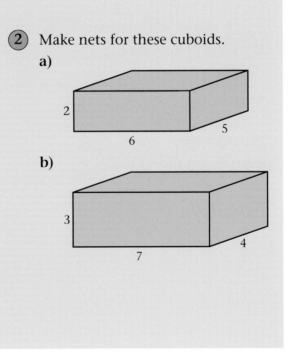

On these pages you will learn to understand and use the terms range, mode, median and mean.

THE RANGE
The difference between the highest value and the lowest value.

THE MODE
The most common value.

THE MEDIAN
The middle value when the numbers are rearranged in order of size.

THE MEAN
The total divided by the number of items in the set.

Example
The marks achieved by 9 children in a test:
8   4   7   1   8   9   3   8   6

The *range* of marks is 8.
Highest − Lowest = 9 − 1
                         = 8

The *mode* is 8.
Eight occurs three times.

The *median* is 7.
1   3   4   6   (7)   8   8   8   9

The *mean* is 6.
Total marks ÷ no. of children = 54 ÷ 9
                                            = 6

Ⓜ
For each of the following sets of data find:
a) the range
b) the mode
c) the median.

① The ages of five friends.
   11   9   7   11   10

② The goals scored by 11 footballers in one season.
   0   2   1   0   1   7
       3   12   4   1   2

③ The daily maximum temperatures recorded in one week in March.

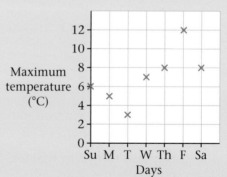

④ The daily hours of sunshine recorded in the same week.

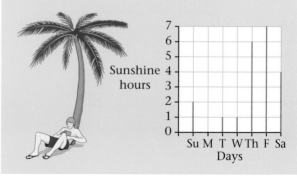

E

For each of the following sets of data find:

a) the range   c) the median

b) the mode   d) the mean.

1 The ages of 15 children at a birthday party.

2 5 7 3 4 3 6 2
3 5 6 4 5 2 3

2 The lengths in seconds for which a new surfer stayed on his board.

3 2 8 4 3 12 5
7 15 3 10 2 4

3 The daily maximum temperatures recorded in one week in May.

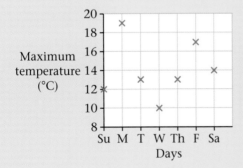

4 Joanne's marks in her weekly maths test.

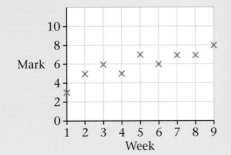

1+1=2

(1) Write down the missing number for each box.

$$250 + \boxed{} = 600$$
$$192 - \boxed{} = 80$$

(2) Work out 479 + 351

(3) Work out 524 − 249

(4) Sarah had £7·65. She bought some fruit costing £2·28.
How much money did she have left?

(5) Javed, Emma and Tina buy some chocolate.
This is what they pay.

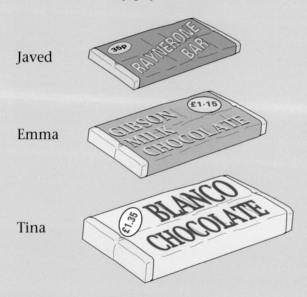

Javed

Emma

Tina

a) How much **more** does **Tina** pay than Javed?

Emma buys another chocolate bar for 80p.

b) How much has Emma paid altogether for her two chocolate bars?

(6) Here is a number sequence.

86   77   68   59   □   □

Write down the missing numbers for each box.

(7) Here is a number sequence

1   3   6   10   □

a) Write down the missing number.

b) Explain how you worked it out.

(8) Use a ruler to measure the perimeter of this picture.

(9) Measure the length of this line to the nearest millimetre.

(10) A number multiplied by itself gives the answer 64. Is this number (5) (6) (7) (8) or (9)?

(11) The numbers 4, 13 and 18 are dropped into this sorting machine. Which bucket will each one fall into?

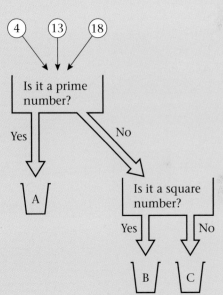

(12) This chart shows the temperatures in four cities.

Birmingham	1°C
Leeds	−4°C
London	2°C
Manchester	−6°C

Find the **difference** between the temperatures in Manchester and Birmingham.

(13) Write these numbers in order of size, starting with the smallest.

| 5 | −4 | −1 |

| 1 | −2 |

(14) Tom needs $\frac{1}{2}$ litre of cream when he
is making some ice cream.
He has a 400 ml pot of cream in
the fridge.
Will he have enough cream?

(15)

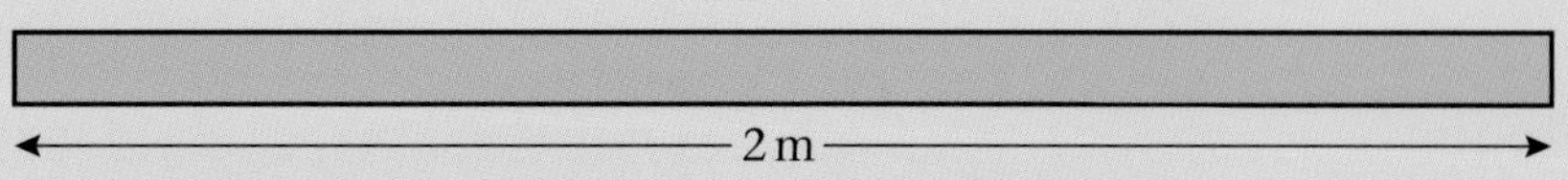

David has a 2 metre piece of wood.
If he cuts off 32 cm, how much wood will he have left?

(16) Match each shape on the left to one with **equal area** on the right.
One has been done for you.

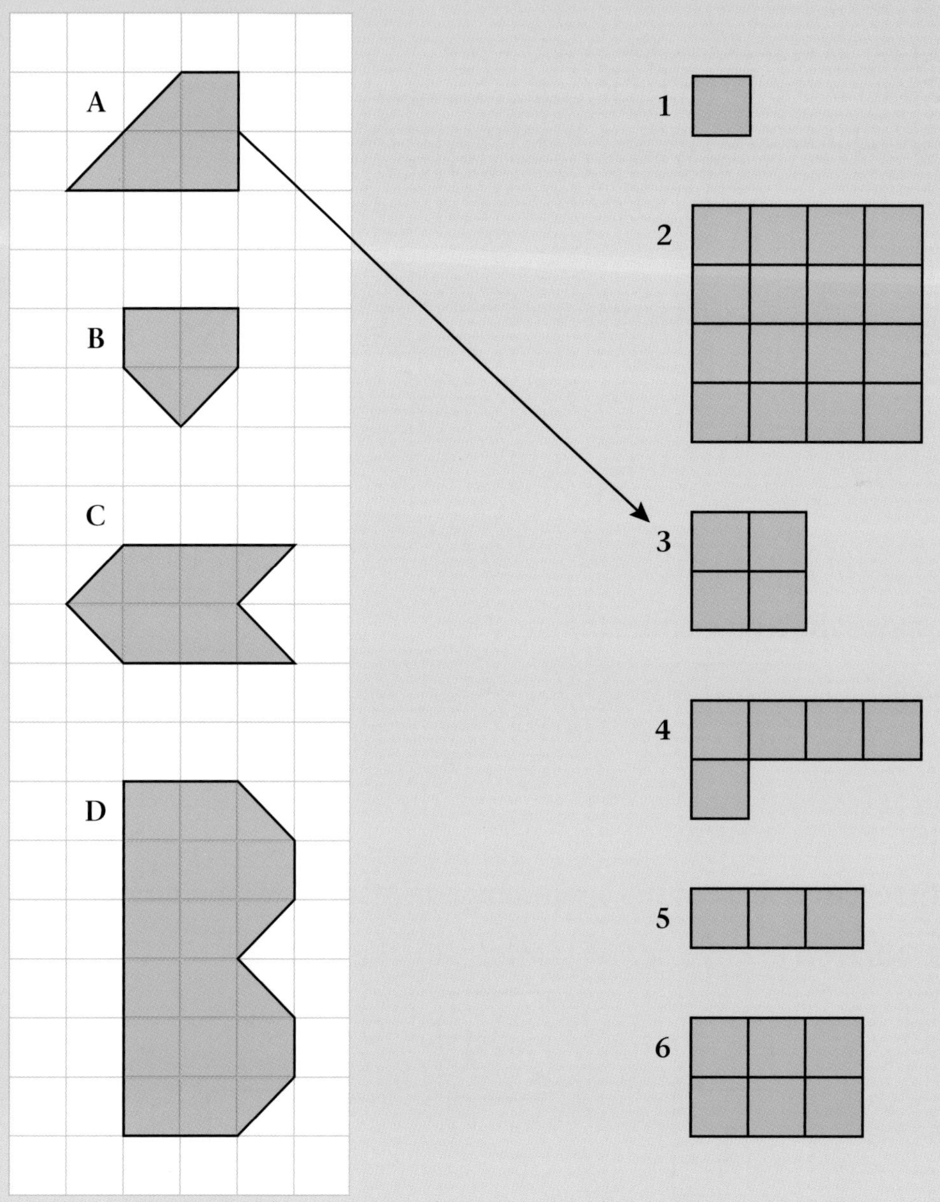

A

B

C

D

1

2

3

4

5

6

(17) The number of CDs owned by 5 friends is

11   5   10   4   10

    a) Find the median number of CDs.

    b) Find the mean number of CDs.

(18)

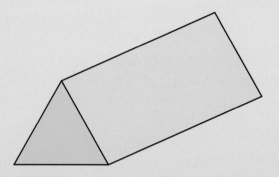

How many **vertices** (corners) does this triangular prism have?
Remember you cannot see them all on this picture.

(19) Work out 30×100.

(20) If nine children were each given £7, how much money would they get in total?

On this page you will work out magic squares.

Example

4	9	2
3	5	7
8	1	6

In a magic square the sum of each row, column and diagonal is the same.

(↔) Rows (↔)	(↕) Columns (↕)	(↗) Diagonals (↘)
4 + 9 + 2 = 15	4 + 3 + 8 = 15	4 + 5 + 6 = 15
3 + 5 + 7 = 15	9 + 5 + 1 = 15	8 + 5 + 2 = 15
8 + 1 + 6 = 15	2 + 7 + 6 = 15	

Copy and complete the magic squares.

1

6	5	
11		
4		

4

3		
	8	
7		13

7

16		
8		
15		10

2

3	10	5
	2	

5

		10
		3
	5	14

8

12	16	
20		
13		

3

6		
	5	
	3	4

6

	14	
11	6	13

9

		11
	12	8
13		

The Four Operations 1

On this page you will use + − × ÷.

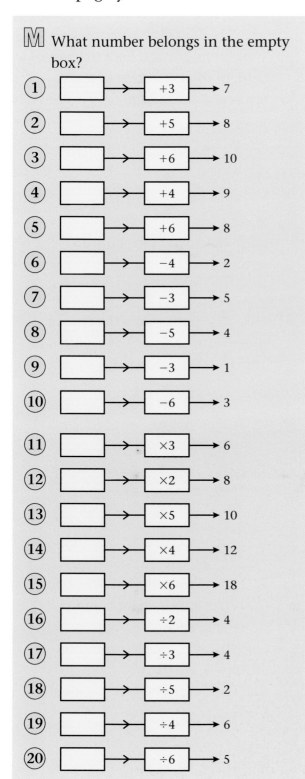

M What number belongs in the empty box?

1. □ → +3 → 7
2. □ → +5 → 8
3. □ → +6 → 10
4. □ → +4 → 9
5. □ → +6 → 8
6. □ → −4 → 2
7. □ → −3 → 5
8. □ → −5 → 4
9. □ → −3 → 1
10. □ → −6 → 3
11. □ → ×3 → 6
12. □ → ×2 → 8
13. □ → ×5 → 10
14. □ → ×4 → 12
15. □ → ×6 → 18
16. □ → ÷2 → 4
17. □ → ÷3 → 4
18. □ → ÷5 → 2
19. □ → ÷4 → 6
20. □ → ÷6 → 5

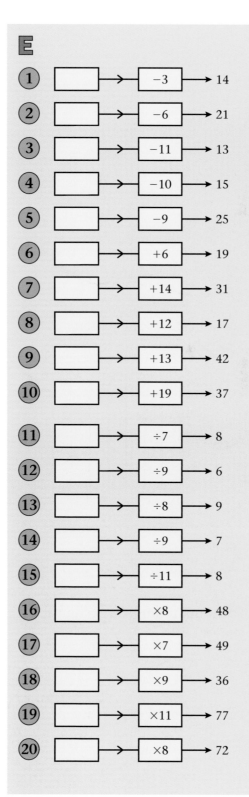

E

1. □ → −3 → 14
2. □ → −6 → 21
3. □ → −11 → 13
4. □ → −10 → 15
5. □ → −9 → 25
6. □ → +6 → 19
7. □ → +14 → 31
8. □ → +12 → 17
9. □ → +13 → 42
10. □ → +19 → 37
11. □ → ÷7 → 8
12. □ → ÷9 → 6
13. □ → ÷8 → 9
14. □ → ÷9 → 7
15. □ → ÷11 → 8
16. □ → ×8 → 48
17. □ → ×7 → 49
18. □ → ×9 → 36
19. □ → ×11 → 77
20. □ → ×8 → 72

On these pages you will learn: ● to make a frequency table.

   ● to make and interpret a bar chart.

Ⓜ

① The members of a football club voted for the colour of their new kit. They chose from red, blue, gold and white. These are the results of the vote.

G   B   G   R   W   G   B   R
R   W   R   G   G   B   R   G
G   R   G   B   R   W   G   R
B   G   W   R   G   R   B   G

Make a frequency table and then draw a bar chart to show the results.

② This graph shows the passengers on a bus.

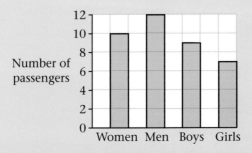

a)   How many women were on the bus?
b)   How many boys were on the bus?
c)   How many adults were on the bus?
d)   How many more women than girls were passengers?
e)   How many passengers were there altogether?

③ The children on a school trip had brought these numbers of apple, blackcurrant, cola and orange drinks.

C   C   B   O   B   A   C   B
O   C   O   C   O   B   O   A
C   O   B   A   C   O   C   C
C   O   C   O   B   A   C   O

Make a frequency table and then draw a pictogram to show the results.

④ This pictogram shows the type of shoes worn to school by children in Year 1.

Boots   🧍 🧍 🧍 🧍 🧍

Sandals   🧍 🧍

School shoes 🧍 🧍 🧍 🧍 🧍 🧍

Trainers   🧍 🧍 🧍 🧍 🧍 🧍 🧍

🧍 represents 2 children

a)   How many children wore boots?
b)   What was the most common type of shoe?
c)   What was the least common type of shoe?
d)   How many children are there in Year 1?

E

1 The children in Year 7 were asked how they came to school. It was found that they walked or came by car, bus or train. These are the results.

```
C  B  W  C  T  W  C  C
C  W  C  B  W  C  T  W
B  C  T  C  W  W  B  C
C  C  W  W  C  B  C  W
C  W  B  C  T  C  W  C
```

Make a frequency table and then draw a bar chart to show the results.

2 This graph shows the number of children walking to school in each year group.

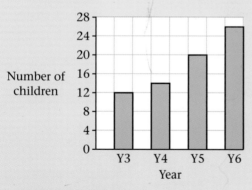

a) How many children walked to school in Year 4?

b) How many more children walked to school in Year 5 than in Year 3?

c) How many children walked to school altogether?

d) In which Year did most children walk to school? Why do you think this was?

3 In one day a sweet shop sold these numbers of packets of chocolate, fruit, mint and toffee sweets.

```
T  C  F  G  T  M  C  T  F  C
C  F  M  T  C  F  C  M  T  F
M  C  F  C  T  T  F  C  M  T
T  F  C  M  C  T  M  F  T  C
T  C  F  M  C  F  T  T  F  C
```

Make a frequency table and then draw a pictogram to show the results.

4 This pictogram shows the number of snails found by a gardener on his cabbages.

Wednesday	☺ ☺ ☺ ☺ ☺ ☺ ☺ ☺
Thursday	☺ ☺ ☺ ☺ ☺ ☺
Friday	☺ ☺ ☺ ☺
Saturday	☺ ☺ ☺

☺ represents 5 snails

a) How many snails were found on Thursday?

b) How many more snails were found on Thursday than on Friday?

c) How many fewer snails were found on Saturday than on Wednesday?

d) How many snails were found altogether?

e) On which day were least snails found? Can you explain why?

On these pages you will learn to use the language associated with probability.

The probability of something happening is the likelihood or chance that it might happen.

Examples

What is the probability of these events?

(1) The sun will rise tomorrow.

(2) You will live to be 500.

(3) You spin a coin and get a head.

(4) It will rain tomorrow.

(5) You will see 4 penguins on your way home.

(6) You will see an ambulance on your way home.

The probabilities of these events can be placed on a scale. You might choose to place them in these positions.

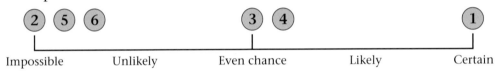

| Impossible | Unlikely | Even chance | Likely | Certain |

M

For each of these statements write one of these probabilities.

certain   *likely*   *even chance*   *unlikely*   *impossible*

(1) You will get married next week.

(2) You will watch television this evening.

(3) The next match a football team play will be a home game.

(4) Your teacher will win the Lottery and retire to the Bahamas.

(5) You will have a birthday in the next year.

(6) You roll a dice and get a 6.

(7) The phone will ring this evening.

(8) You will have a new pair of shoes in the next three months.

(9) You will learn to juggle in the next year.

(10) It will snow next week.

E

Discuss the probability of these events.
Place them on a scale like the one on the previous page.

(1) You will get married when you grow up.

(2) The Queen was born on a Thursday.

(3) Someone in the family will receive a letter tomorrow.

(4) You will pass your driving test next year.

(5) You roll a dice and get an even number.

(6) The next person to come into the classroom will be the Headteacher.

(7) A baby will be born somewhere in the world today.

(8) Everyone in the class will watch television next week.

(9) You will see a snail on your way home today.

(10) A teacher at your school will have a Number 1 hit record.

(11) Place the ten events in Section M on a new scale.

On these pages you will work out the probability (chance) of some events happening.

Examples

There are four identical beads in a bag.

I take out one bead.

The probability of taking out (V) is $\frac{1}{4}$ ← one in the bag
← 4 beads in total

The probability of taking out (E) is also $\frac{1}{4}$

---

1 There are five identical beads in a bag.

I take out one bead.
a) Work out the probability of taking out (H).
b) Work out the probability of taking out (M).

2 There are four identical beads in a bag. I take out one bead.

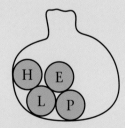

a) Work out the probability of taking out (P).
b) Work out the probability of taking out (L).

3 Work out the probability of spinning a coin and getting a head.

4 0 |___|___|___|___|___|___| 1

Copy this probability scale.

Work out the probabilities of the following as fractions and write the letter in the correct place on your line:
a) rolling a dice and getting a 4.
b) rolling a dice and getting a 1 or a 3.
c) spinning a coin and getting a tail.
d) spinning a coin and getting a tail or a head.

5 There are four identical beads in a bag.

I take out one bead.
Work out the probability of taking (Y).

6 8 football clubs are in the draw for the quarter-finals of the F.A. Cup.

Arsenal   Liverpool
Newcastle Utd   West Ham Utd
Everton   Leeds Utd
Manchester Utd   Manchester City

What is the probability that the first club to be chosen will be West Ham?

E

1 There are six identical beads in a bag.

(H) (A) (R) (D) (E) (R)

I take out one bead.

Work out the probability of taking out (R).

2 There are seven identical beads in a bag.
I take out one bead.

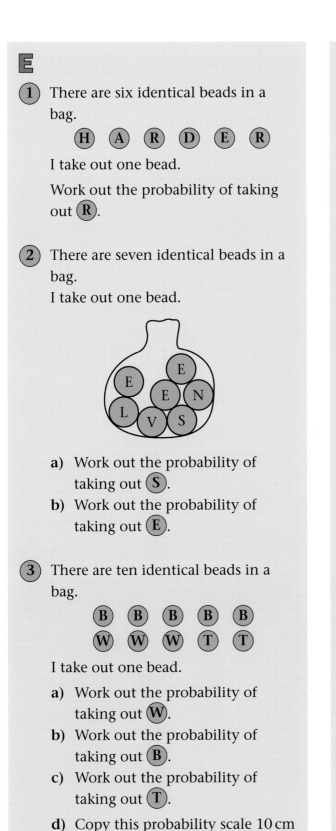

a) Work out the probability of taking out (S).

b) Work out the probability of taking out (E).

3 There are ten identical beads in a bag.

(B) (B) (B) (B) (B)
(W) (W) (W) (T) (T)

I take out one bead.

a) Work out the probability of taking out (W).

b) Work out the probability of taking out (B).

c) Work out the probability of taking out (T).

d) Copy this probability scale 10 cm long and show your answers to **a)**, **b)** and **c)** in the correct place on your line.

0 ├─┼─┼─┼─┼─┼─┼─┼─┼─┤ 1

4 Work out the probabilities of:

a) rolling a dice and getting a 5.

b) rolling a dice and getting 3, 4 or 5.

c) rolling a dice and getting an even number.

5 Copy this probability scale,

0 ├─┼─┼─┼─┼─┼─┼─┼─┼─┼─┼─┼─┼─┤ 1
                    $\frac{1}{2}$

There are 20 beads in a bag.

10 beads are blue.
3 beads are red.
2 beads are green.
5 beads are yellow.

I take out one bead.
Find the probability of:

a) taking out a red bead.

b) taking out a blue bead.

c) taking out a yellow bead.

d) taking out a green bead.

e) taking out a blue or red bead.

f) taking out a black bead.

g) Show all your answers on your probability scale.

6 There are 25 identical fish in a tank.

8 fish are gold.

12 fish are red.

The rest of the fish are yellow.

I catch one fish.

Find the probability of:

a) catching a red fish.

b) catching a gold fish.

c) catching a yellow or red fish.

d) catching a gold, yellow or red fish.

e) Draw your own probability scale to show all these answers.

On these pages you will learn to recognise fractions.

A fraction is a number that is less than a whole one.
When a whole one is divided into equal parts each of the parts is a fraction of the whole one.

Examples

2 equal parts

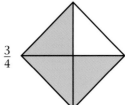

$\frac{1}{2}$

one half is shaded

4 equal parts

$\frac{3}{4}$

three quarters is shaded

10 equal parts

$\frac{7}{10}$

seven tenths is shaded

Write one half, one quarter or three quarters for each shape.
Write your answers in both words and figures.

① 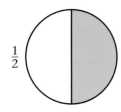   ③   ⑤   ⑦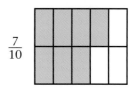

②   ④   ⑥   ⑧

③   ⑥   ⑨   ⑭

Copy and complete these sentences by writing the fractions in words.

⑨ ☐ of the shapes on the right are circles.

⑩ ☐ of the shapes are black.

⑪ ☐ of the shapes are triangles.

⑫ ☐ of the shapes are not squares.

⑬ ☐ of the shapes have four sides.

⑭ ☐ of the shapes are not circles.

49

What fraction of each diagram is shaded?
Write your answer in both words and figures.

(15) 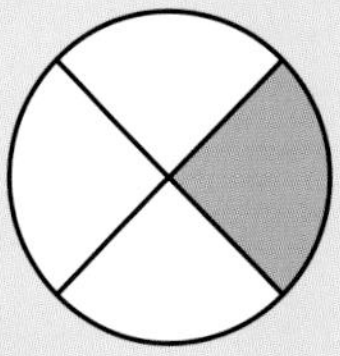　(17) 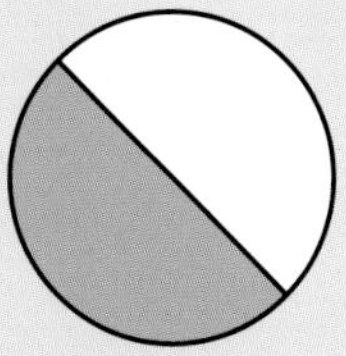　(19) 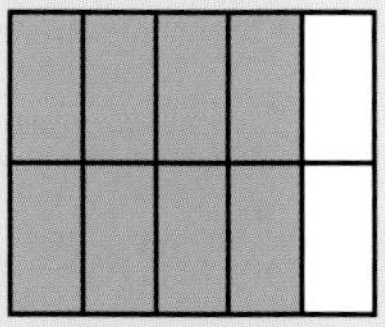　(21)

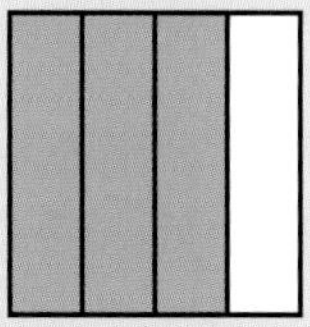

(16) 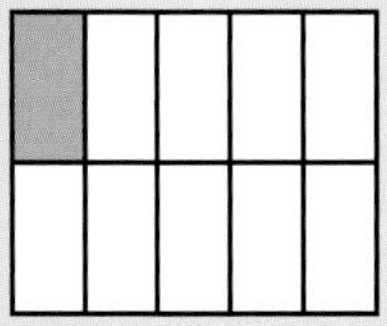　(18) 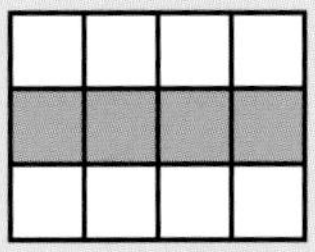　(20) 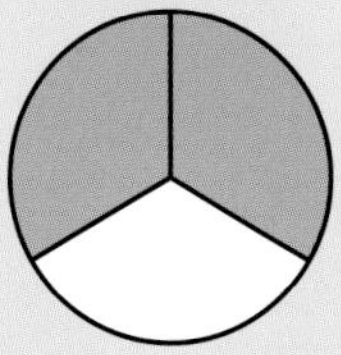　(22)

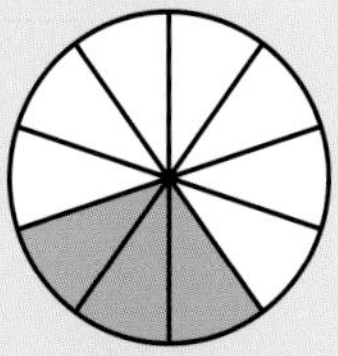

What fractions are shown on each of these number lines?

(23) 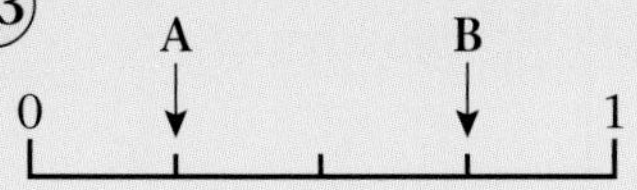
A　　　B
0　↓　↓　1

(24) 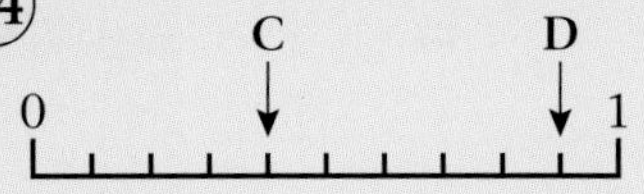
C　　　D
0　　↓　↓1

(25) 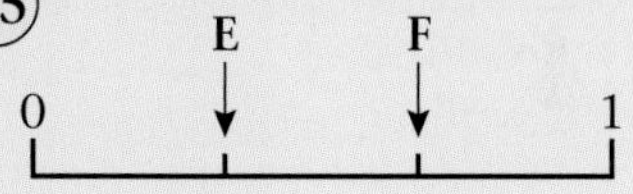
E　　F
0　↓　↓　1

E

What fraction of each diagram is:
a) shaded　　b) unshaded?
Write your answers in figures and in words.

(1) 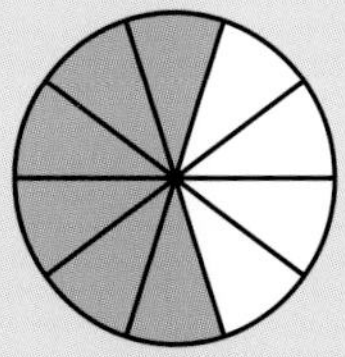　(4) 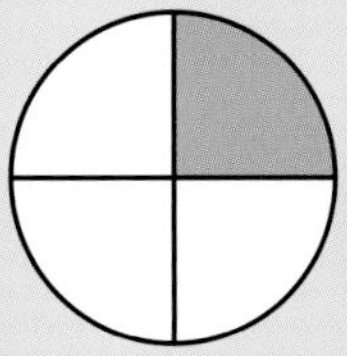　(7) 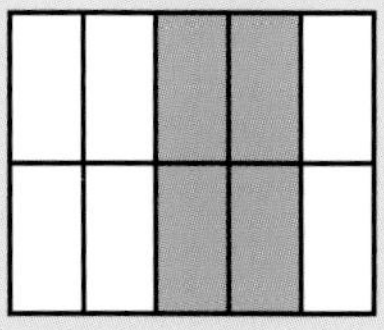　(10)

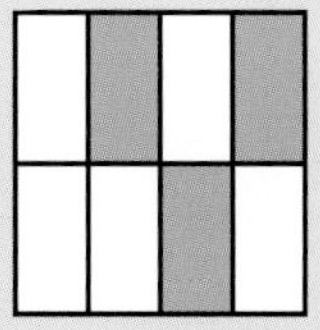

(2) 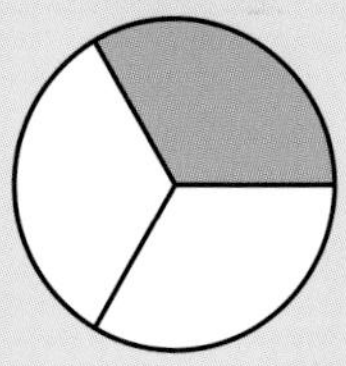　(5) 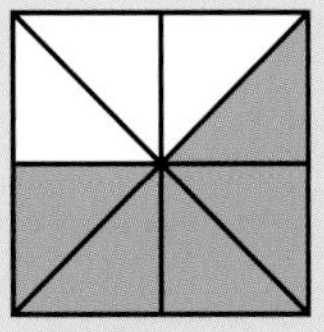　(8) 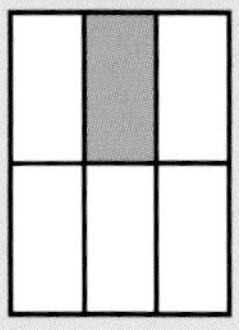　(11)

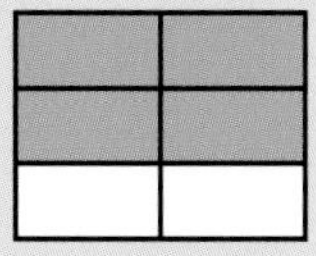

(3) 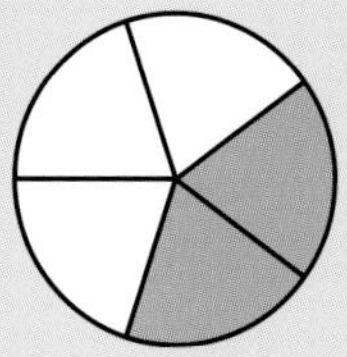　(6) 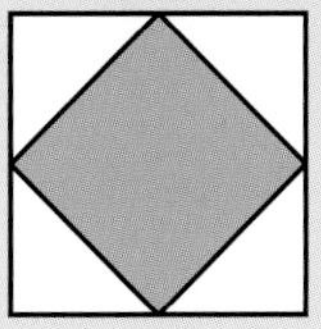　(9) 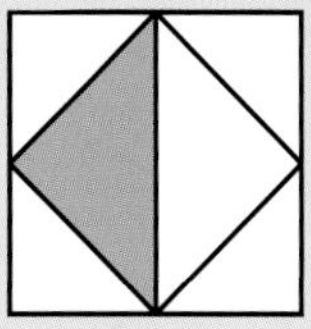　(12)

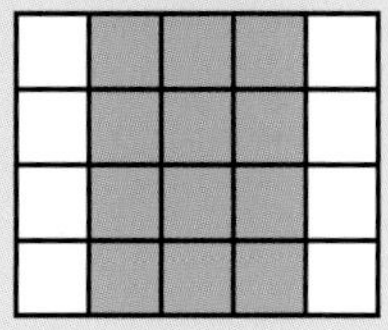

(13) Draw two grids like the one shown.
　　a) Shade in $\frac{2}{3}$ of the squares.
　　b) Put × in $\frac{3}{4}$ of the squares.

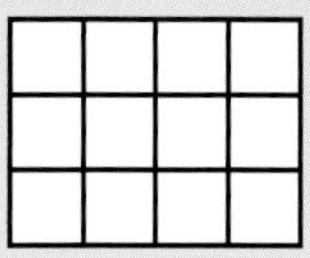

On these pages you will learn to recognise equivalent fractions.

Equivalent fractions are fractions that look different but are the same.

Examples

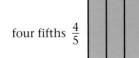 one half $\frac{1}{2}$ =   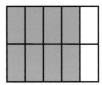 $\frac{2}{4}$ two quarters

four fifths $\frac{4}{5}$ = $\frac{8}{10}$ eight tenths

Ⓜ **Part 1**

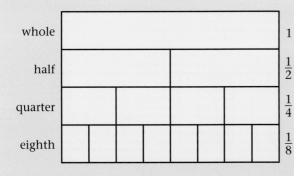

whole	1
half	$\frac{1}{2}$
quarter	$\frac{1}{4}$
eighth	$\frac{1}{8}$

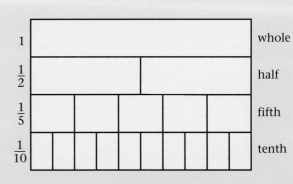

1	whole
$\frac{1}{2}$	half
$\frac{1}{5}$	fifth
$\frac{1}{10}$	tenth

Use the fraction charts to copy and complete by filling in the box.

① $\frac{1}{2} = \frac{\square}{4}$ ④ $1 = \frac{\square}{5}$ ⑦ $1 = \frac{\square}{4}$ ⑩ $\frac{3}{5} = \frac{\square}{10}$

② $1 = \frac{\square}{8}$ ⑤ $\frac{3}{4} = \frac{\square}{8}$ ⑧ $\frac{1}{4} = \frac{\square}{8}$ ⑪ $\frac{1}{2} = \frac{\square}{8}$

③ $\frac{1}{5} = \frac{\square}{10}$ ⑥ $\frac{1}{2} = \frac{\square}{10}$ ⑨ $1 = \frac{\square}{2}$ ⑫ $1 = \frac{\square}{10}$

Copy and complete these fraction chains.

⑬ $\frac{1}{2} = \frac{\square}{4} = \frac{\square}{8} = \frac{\square}{16}$ ⑭ $\frac{1}{2} = \frac{\square}{4} = \frac{\square}{6} = \frac{\square}{8} = \frac{\square}{10}$

Part 2

Use squared paper.

Draw a fraction chart to show a whole one, thirds, sixths and twelfths.

Use your chart to complete these equivalent fractions.

① $\frac{1}{2} = \frac{\square}{6}$ ④ $\frac{2}{3} = \frac{\square}{6}$ ⑦ $\frac{1}{3} = \frac{\square}{12}$ ⑩ $1 = \frac{\square}{12}$

② $\frac{1}{3} = \frac{\square}{6}$ ⑤ $\frac{5}{6} = \frac{\square}{12}$ ⑧ $\frac{4}{6} = \frac{\square}{12}$ ⑪ $\frac{2}{3} = \frac{\square}{12}$

③ $\frac{1}{6} = \frac{\square}{12}$ ⑥ $1 = \frac{\square}{6}$ ⑨ $\frac{1}{2} = \frac{\square}{12}$ ⑫ $\frac{2}{6} = \frac{\square}{12}$

Which is the odd one out in each set of fractions?

⑬ $\left(\frac{3}{7} \quad \frac{2}{4} \quad \frac{1}{2} \quad \frac{4}{8} \quad \frac{5}{10} \right)$ ⑮ $\left(\frac{10}{15} \quad \frac{3}{6} \quad \frac{2}{3} \quad \frac{8}{12} \quad \frac{6}{9} \right)$

⑭ $\left(\frac{1}{5} \quad \frac{2}{10} \quad \frac{10}{50} \quad \frac{5}{20} \quad \frac{3}{15} \right)$ ⑯ $\left(\frac{2}{8} \quad \frac{10}{40} \quad \frac{8}{16} \quad \frac{3}{12} \quad \frac{1}{4} \right)$

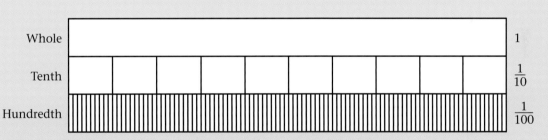

Whole		1
Tenth		$\frac{1}{10}$
Hundredth		$\frac{1}{100}$

Use the fraction chart to copy and complete by filling in the box.

① $\frac{2}{10} = \frac{\square}{100}$ ④ $\frac{10}{100} = \frac{\square}{10}$ ⑦ $\frac{8}{10} = \frac{\square}{100}$

② $\frac{5}{10} = \frac{\square}{100}$ ⑤ $\frac{70}{100} = \frac{\square}{10}$ ⑧ $\frac{6}{10} = \frac{\square}{100}$

③ $\frac{30}{100} = \frac{\square}{10}$ ⑥ $1 = \frac{\square}{10}$ ⑨ $\frac{40}{100} = \frac{\square}{10}$

Which is the odd one out in each set of fractions?

⑩ $\left(\frac{5}{10} \quad \frac{15}{100} \quad \frac{50}{100} \quad \frac{1}{2} \right)$ ⑫ $\left(\frac{7}{20} \quad \frac{7}{10} \quad \frac{70}{100} \right)$

⑪ $\left(\frac{10}{10} \quad \frac{2}{2} \quad 1 \quad \frac{20}{10} \right)$ ⑬ $\left(\frac{1}{10} \quad \frac{10}{100} \quad \frac{1}{4} \right)$

On these pages you will learn to understand percentage as the number of parts in 100. You will practise writing $\frac{1}{2}$, $\frac{1}{4}$, $\frac{3}{4}$, tenths and hundredths as percentages.

Per cent means `out of 100'.

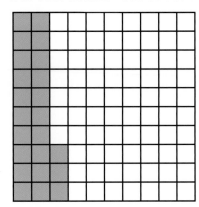

23 out of 100 small squares are shaded.

Fraction shaded $= \dfrac{23}{100}$

Percentage shaded = 23%.

M

1 ----------- 100%

$\frac{3}{4}$ ----------- 75%

$\frac{1}{2}$ ----------- 50%

$\frac{1}{4}$ ----------- 25%

0 ----------- 0%

This is a beaker.

Look at the beakers below.
Copy and complete the sentences.

①

1

$\frac{3}{4}$

$\frac{1}{2}$

$\frac{1}{4}$

0

This beaker is a quarter full
so it is ☐ % full.

②

1

$\frac{3}{4}$

$\frac{1}{2}$

$\frac{1}{4}$

0

This beaker is three quarters full
so it is ☐ % full.

③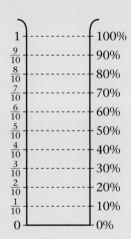

This beaker is a half full
so it is [   ] % full.

④ What percentage is equivalent to 1?

⑤ What fraction is equivalent to 50%?

⑥ What fraction is equivalent to 25%?

⑦ What percentage is equivalent to $\frac{3}{4}$?

⑧ 40% is more than $\frac{1}{4}$. True or false?

⑨ 80% is more than $\frac{3}{4}$. True or false?

⑩ 49% is more than $\frac{1}{2}$. True or false?

Here is another beaker.
10% means $\frac{1}{10}$
30% means $\frac{3}{10}$

⑪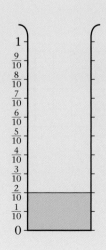

This beaker is two-tenths full
so it is [   ] % full.

54

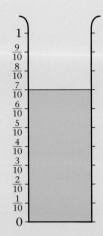

⑫ This beaker is seven-tenths full so it is ☐ % full.

⑬ What percentage is equivalent to $\frac{1}{10}$?

⑭ What percentage is equivalent to $\frac{3}{10}$?

⑮ What fraction is equivalent to 20%?

⑯ What fraction is equivalent to 90%?

⑰ What percentage is equivalent to $\frac{6}{10}$?

⑱ What fraction is equivalent to 70%?

⑲ 31% is more than $\frac{4}{10}$. True or false?

⑳ 68% is more than $\frac{6}{10}$. True or false?

E

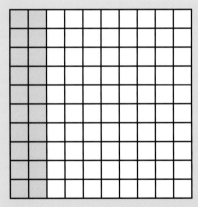

20 out of 100 small squares are shaded.

Fraction shaded $= \frac{20}{100}$

Percentage shaded = 20%.

You can also see that 20 out of 100 small squares is $\frac{1}{5}$ of 100% because 100% cut up into 5 parts is 20%.

$\frac{1}{5} = 20\%$ because $\frac{1}{5}$ of 100 = 20.

For each diagram, write down the shaded area as:

a) a fraction

b) a percentage

①

②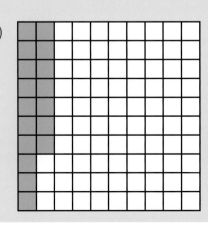

③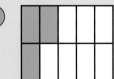

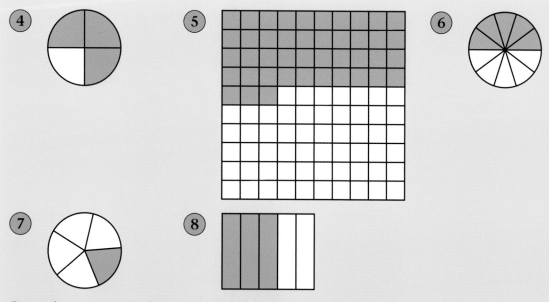

Copy the sentences changing each fraction to a percentage:

9 *One tenth* of the cars were blue.

10 Ellie has read *three quarters* of her book.

11 *Seven tenths* of the class saw the programme.

12 One pence is *one hundredth* of one pound.

13 Bruce lost *one fifth* of his golf balls.

The pictures below show how much petrol is in a car. For each picture write down what percentage is in each car and what percentage has been used if the petrol tank was full to start with.

19 In a survey about favourite sports, one quarter ($\frac{1}{4}$) of the people voted for cricket. What percentage of the people did not vote for cricket?

20 In the same sports survey, four fifths ($\frac{4}{5}$) of the people voted for football. What percentage of the people voted for football?

On these pages you will learn how to find percentages of small amounts.

Examples

a) 10% of 80

$= \frac{1}{10}$ of 80

$= 8$

b) 20% of 80

FIND 10% FIRST

10% of 80 = 8

DOUBLE THIS ANSWER GIVES 20%

20% of 80 = 8 × 2

$= 16$

c) 30% of 80

FIND 10% FIRST

10% of 80 = 8

3 × 10% GIVES 30%

30% of 80 = 8 × 3

$= 24$

d) 25% of 80

WE KNOW 25% is $\frac{1}{4}$

$\frac{1}{4}$ of 80 = 80 ÷ 4

$= 20$

Ⓜ

①

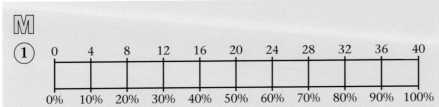

a) Find 10% of 40

b) Find 20% of 40

c) Find 50% of 40

d) Find 70% of 40

e) Find 30% of 40

f) Find 80% of 40

g) Find 100% of 40

h) Find 5% of 40

Remember: 25% = $\frac{1}{4}$

50% = $\frac{1}{2}$

75% = $\frac{3}{4}$

② Find 10% of:

a) 30   d) 20

b) 90   e) 100

c) 60   f) 70

③ Find 20% of:

a) 20   d) 50

b) 30   e) 60

c) 100   f) 150

④ Find 30% of:

a) 60   d) 90

b) 20   e) 120

c) 70   f) 200

⑤ Find 70% of:

a) 20   d) 80

b) 50   e) 70

c) 30   f) 200

⑥ Find 5% of:

a) 20   d) 140

b) 200   e) 40

c) 60   f) 300

⑦ Find 50% of:

a) 18   d) 200

b) 50   e) 48

c) 42   f) 70

⑧ Find 25% of:

a) 12   d) 64

b) 36   e) 48

c) 80   f) 120

⑨ Find 75% of:

a) 12   c) 40

b) 20   d) 28

⑩ Find:

a) 10% of £400

b) 40% of £400

c) 60% of £300

d) 30% of £700

E

Work out

(1) 10% of 60

(6) 75% of 32

(11) 10% of £1·40

(2) 50% of 36

(7) 40% of 80

(12) 25% of £1·20

(3) 25% of 44

(8) 50% of £3

(13) 30% of 70p

(4) 30% of 120

(9) 20% of 20p

(14) 40% of £1·50

(5) 10% of 200

(10) 10% of £640

(15) 50% of £6·20

Sometimes shop prices are reduced by a percentage.

Example

Shirt £30
SALE
20% off

How much is the price reduced by?
20% of £30 = 3 × 2 = £6
　　　　　　　↑
　　　　　　 10%

What is the sale price?
Shirt £30 − £6　　=　　£24
　　　　　 ↑　　　　　　 ↑
　　　 reduction　　 sale price

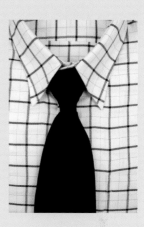

For each question, answer the following:

a) How much is the price reduced by?

b) What is the sale price?

(16)
TV £400
SALE
10% off

(19)
Trousers £40
SALE
30% discount

(22)
Shirt £20
SALE
5% off

(17)
Jacket £60
SALE
20% off

(20)
CD £16
SALE
Price reduced by 25%

(23)
Skateboard £48
SALE
25% discount

(18)
CD Player £90
SALE
50% off

(21)
Computer £800
SALE
20% off

(24)
Computer Game £32
SALE
Price reduced by 75%

On these pages you will learn to recognise decimal fractions and learn the value of the digits in a decimal fraction.

Decimals are a way of expressing fractions. The decimal point separates the whole number from the fractions.

Examples

$2\frac{3}{10} = 2\cdot3$

$1\frac{53}{100} = 1\cdot53$

The value of a digit depends upon its position in a number.

Each digit in a number is 10 times higher than the digit to the right. This applies to decimal fractions as well as to whole numbers.

Examples

$$
\begin{array}{rccc}
 & \text{T} & \text{U}\cdot\frac{1}{10} & \frac{1}{100} \\
30 = 3 & 0 & \cdot\,0 & \\
3 = & 3 & \cdot\,0 & \\
\frac{3}{10} = & & 0\cdot3 & \\
\frac{3}{100} = & & 0\cdot0 & 3 \\
\end{array}
$$

$$
\begin{array}{rcccc}
 & \text{H} & \text{T} & \text{U}\cdot\frac{1}{10} & \frac{1}{100} \\
700 = 7 & 0 & 0 & \cdot\,0 & \\
70 = & & 7 & 0\cdot0 & \\
7 = & & & 7\cdot0 & \\
\frac{7}{10} = & & & 0\cdot7 & \\
\frac{7}{100} = & & & 0\cdot0 & 7 \\
\end{array}
$$

Part 1

What part of each shape is shaded? Write your answer as a fraction and as a decimal fraction.

① 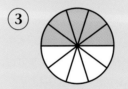 ⑥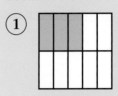

② 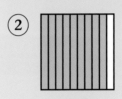 ⑦

③ 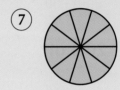 ⑧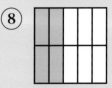

④ 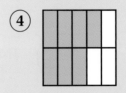 ⑨

⑤  ⑩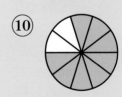

Write the numbers shown by each of the arrows on the 0 to 1 number line as:
a) a fraction.
b) a decimal fraction.

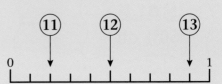

Part 2

Write each number shown by the arrows as a decimal fraction.

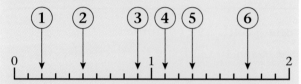

Give the value of the underlined figure in each of these numbers.

(7) 6.**8**

(8) 1**4**.9

(9) 0.**7**

(10) **5**.3

(11) **1**8.2

(12) 24.**1**

(13) **3**.07

(14) 8.**6**4

(15) 19.**3**2

(16) 12.**4**6

(17) 0.**5**2

(18) 10**6**.8

Give the next five terms in each of these sequences.

(19) 0.1   0.2   0.3   0.4   0.5

(20) 0.2   0.4   0.6   0.8   1.0

(21) 0.5   1.0   1.5   2.0   2.5

(22) 0.1   0.3   0.5   0.7   0.9

What part of each shape is shaded? Write your answer as a fraction and as a decimal fraction.

(23)   (26)

(24)   (27)

(25)   (28)

E

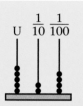

Example

5 units   2 tenths   4 hundredths
The number shown is 5.24.

Write the decimal fraction shown on each abacus.

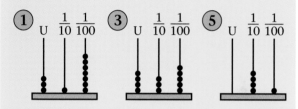

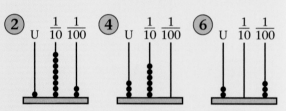

Give the value of the underlined figure in each of these numbers.

(7) 0.**9**

(8) **1**0.4

(9) 2**4**.7

(10) 18.**7**6

(11) 13.**9**1

(12) 2**6**.58

(13) 2.**9**6

(14) **3**5.42

(15) 41.**7**8

(16) 1**7**.49

(17) 7.**3**4

(18) 32.5**7**

(19) 16.**2**3

(20) 25.0**4**

(21) **5**.13

(22) 78.**0**6

(23) 100.8**3**

(24) 136.**5**9

Write the answer only.

(25) 1.5 + 0.4

(26) 2.3 + 0.7

(27) 1.3 − 0.3

(28) 1.6 − 0.7

(29) 3.8 + 0.5

(30) 1.5 + 1.9

(31) 2.4 − 0.6

(32) 1.7 − 0.9

(33) 0.2 + 0.8

(34) 0.6 + 1.1

(35) 1.8 − 1.4

(36) 2.1 − 0.8

(37) 1.8 + 1.6

(38) 2.3 + 0.9

(39) 3.2 − 0.8

(40) 4.5 − 0.6

On this page you will learn to order a set of decimals.

Write the set of decimals in a line with the decimal points in a column.

Fill in any empty spaces with zeros. This makes it easier to compare the decimals.

Example

Arrange 1·4, 0·41, 2 and 1·2 in order.

Write in column.	Put in zeros.	Arrange in order.
1·4	1·40	0·41
0·41	0·41	1·2
2	2·00	1·4
1·2	1·20	2

Ⓜ

Write the larger of these pairs of numbers.

① 16   1·6   ③ 0·8   8·0   ⑤ 1·9   0·9   ⑦ 3·2   2·3   ⑨ 4   1·4

② 1·2   2·0   ④ 5   0·5   ⑥ 1·8   8   ⑧ 0·7   6·7   ⑩ 6·3   3·6

⑪ Copy the line. Put each number from the box on the number line.

| 0·2   0·5   0·9   0·4   0·7 |

0   1

Copy and complete by writing >, < or = in the box.

⑫ 0·6 ☐ 6·0   ⑭ 0·5 ☐ 0·50   ⑯ 46 ☐ 6·4   ⑱ 8·0 ☐ 8

⑬ 14 ☐ 1.4   ⑮ 2·7 ☐ 7·2   ⑰ 1·1 ☐ 11   ⑲ 38 ☐ 8·3

Arrange the decimals in order. Start with the smallest.

⑳ 4·7   7·4   3·6   6·3   ㉒ 21   2·1   1·2   12   ㉔ 8·4   48   8   4·8

㉑ 9·2   2·2   2·9   9·9   ㉓ 5·3   5   3   3·5   ㉕ 7·9   7   7·7   9·7

Ⓔ

Arrange the decimals in order.
Start with the smallest.

① 3·4   33·4   4·3   43·3   43

② 11·9   9·1   9·01   19·1   1·9

③ 14·1   1·4   1·41   11·4   4·1

④ 7·73   8·7   7·83   8·37   8·73

⑤ 9·6   5·69   9·65   9·5   5·96

⑥ Copy the line. Put each number from the box on the number line.

| 0·97   1·08   0·91   1·0   1·05   0·94 |

0.9   1.1

On this page you will learn to find fractions of quantities or numbers.

Examples

| One half of 12p | 12p ÷ 2 = 6p | One tenth of 40p | 40p ÷ 10 = 4p |
| One quarter of 12p | 12p ÷ 4 = 3p | One eighth of 40p | 40p ÷ 8 = 5p |

Ⓜ

Find one half of:

(1) 16   (4) 22

(2) 30   (5) 14

(3) 26   (6) 28

Find one quarter of:

(7) 20 cm   (10) 24 cm

(8) 40 cm   (11) 28 cm

(9) 36 cm   (12) 32 cm

Find one tenth of:

(13) 10p   (16) £1

(14) 50p   (17) 40p

(15) 20p   (18) 70p

(19) Jay has 16 sweets. He eats one quarter of them. How many sweets does he have left?

(20) Alice has 24 books. Three quarters of them are stories. How many of her books are non-fiction?

(21) In a mixed school with 249 pupils, one third of the pupils are girls.
a) How many girls are there?
b) How many boys are there?

Ⓔ

Find

(1) $\frac{1}{2}$ of 100   (7) $\frac{1}{6}$ of 24

(2) $\frac{1}{3}$ of 21   (8) $\frac{1}{5}$ of 45

(3) $\frac{1}{5}$ of 30   (9) $\frac{1}{10}$ of 150

(4) $\frac{1}{8}$ of 16   (10) $\frac{1}{7}$ of 35

(5) $\frac{1}{3}$ of 27   (11) $\frac{1}{3}$ of 18

(6) $\frac{1}{4}$ of 44   (12) $\frac{1}{9}$ of 90

(13) $\frac{1}{10}$ of 60   (16) $\frac{1}{100}$ of 700

(14) $\frac{1}{100}$ of 200   (17) $\frac{1}{10}$ of 80

(15) $\frac{1}{100}$ of 500   (18) $\frac{1}{100}$ of 1000

(19) Find $\frac{1}{100}$ of the following amounts of money:
a) £3   b) £7   c) £4   d) £35
(Hint: Change the pounds into pence first)

(20) Find $\frac{1}{10}$ of the following amounts of money:
a) £3   b) £6   c) £12   d) £24

(21) There are 2500 fish in an aquarium. One fifth of the fish are sold. How many fish are sold?

On these pages you will use decimals, fractions and percentages, doing as much in your head as possible.

Remember

$\frac{81}{100}$ means 81%

Also $\frac{81}{100}$ means 0·81

so 43% = $\frac{43}{100}$ = 0·43

Note.   0·7 = $\frac{7}{10}$ = 70%   ($\frac{7}{10}$ is same as 70%)

77% is $\frac{77}{100}$ or 0.77

M

Change these percentages into fractions:

(1) 50%   (4) 25%   (7) 1%

(2) 60%   (5) 10%   (8) 75%

(3) 3%   (6) 9%   (9) 20%

Change these fractions into percentages:

(10) $\frac{1}{100}$ (13) $\frac{11}{100}$ (16) $\frac{3}{4}$

(11) $\frac{81}{100}$ (14) $\frac{3}{10}$ (17) $\frac{8}{10}$

(12) $\frac{1}{4}$ (15) $\frac{2}{10}$ (18) $\frac{37}{100}$

Change these decimals into fractions:

(19) 0·1   (22) 0·07   (25) 0·25

(20) 0·6   (23) 0·37   (26) 0·8

(21) 0·08   (24) 0·21   (27) 0·63

Change these percentages into decimals:

(28) 2%   (31) 90%   (34) 42%

(29) 1%   (32) 20%   (35) 50%

(30) 9%   (33) 10%   (36) 83%

Change these decimals into percentages:

(37) 0·01   (40) 0·45   (43) 0·75

(38) 0·67   (41) 0·3   (44) 0·61

(39) 0·36   (42) 0·1   (45) 0·8

Change these fractions into decimals:

(46) $\frac{7}{10}$ (49) $\frac{3}{100}$ (52) $\frac{37}{100}$

(47) $\frac{9}{10}$ (50) $\frac{1}{4}$ (53) $\frac{3}{4}$

(48) $\frac{8}{100}$ (51) $\frac{21}{100}$ (54) $\frac{81}{100}$

(55) Copy and complete this table.

fraction	$\frac{1}{4}$			$\frac{13}{100}$	
decimal		0·7			0·99
percentage			75%		

E

1. a) Find 10% of £70.
   b) Find 20% of £70.
   c) Find 70% of £70.

2. a) Find 10% of £60.
   b) Find 5% of £60.
   c) Find 15% of £60.

3. 47% of Year 7 are boys. What percentage of Year 7 are girls?

4. 64% of Year 11 pupils have a mobile phone. What percentage of Year 11 pupils do *not* have a mobile phone?

5. a) Find $\frac{1}{2}$ of £80.
   b) Find $\frac{1}{4}$ of £80.
   c) Find $\frac{3}{4}$ of £80.

6. Jane has 32 sweets. Jack eats $\frac{1}{2}$ of the sweets and Lisa eats $\frac{1}{4}$ of the sweets. How many sweets does Jane have left?

7. Half the children in a school had dark hair and 25% of the children had blond hair. What percentage of children did not have dark hair or blond hair?

8. The course for a kart race is 5000 m long. How far has a kart gone when it has raced 60% of the course?

9. Terry coloured in 0·9 of a shape. What fraction of the shape did he *not* colour in?

10. Fiona spent $\frac{3}{10}$ of her money. What percentage of her money did she have left?

11. 40 pupils go to a sports club. 25% of them are girls. How many of them are boys?

On this page you will learn to change an improper fraction to a mixed number and vice versa.

Examples

1. Change $\frac{7}{3}$ to a mixed number.

   Divide numerator by denominator. $7 \div 3 = 2$ rem. 1

   Put remainder over denominator. $\frac{7}{3} = 2\frac{1}{3}$

2. Change $4\frac{3}{8}$ to an improper fraction.

   Multiply whole number by denominator. $4 \times 8 = 32$

   Add the numerator. $32 + 3 = 35$

   Put sum over denominator. $4\frac{3}{8} = \frac{35}{8}$

M

Write the shaded areas as both mixed numbers and improper fractions.

① ◯ ◯ ◯ ◯ ◯

② ◯ ◯ ◯

③ ◯ ◯ ◯ ◯

④ ◯ ◯

⑤ ◯ ◯ ◯

⑥ ◯ ◯ ◯ ◯ ◯

⑦ ◯ ◯ ◯ ◯

⑧ ◯ ◯

⑨ ◯ ◯ ◯

⑩ ◯ ◯ ◯ ◯ ◯

⑪ ◯ ◯ ◯ ◯

⑫ ◯ ◯ ◯

Copy and complete.

⑬ $3\frac{1}{2} = \frac{7}{\square}$

⑭ $2\frac{2}{3} = \frac{8}{\square}$

⑮ $5\frac{1}{4} = \frac{\square}{4}$

⑯ $4\frac{3}{5} = \frac{\square}{5}$

⑰ $3\frac{7}{10} = \frac{\square}{\square}$

⑱ $2\frac{5}{6} = \frac{\square}{\square}$

⑲ $\frac{5}{3} = 1\frac{\square}{3}$

⑳ $\frac{7}{4} = \square\frac{3}{4}$

㉑ $\frac{19}{6} = \square\frac{\square}{6}$

㉒ $\frac{29}{10} = \square\frac{\square}{10}$

㉓ $\frac{25}{8} = \square\frac{\square}{\square}$

㉔ $\frac{421}{100} = \square\frac{\square}{\square}$

E

Change to mixed numbers.

① $\frac{25}{4}$ ⑦ $\frac{19}{3}$

② $\frac{17}{3}$ ⑧ $\frac{29}{4}$

③ $\frac{29}{5}$ ⑨ $\frac{23}{3}$

④ $\frac{37}{5}$ ⑩ $\frac{50}{8}$

⑤ $\frac{44}{5}$ ⑪ $\frac{57}{9}$

⑥ $\frac{17}{2}$ ⑫ $\frac{92}{10}$

Change to improper fractions.

⑬ $2\frac{1}{2}$ ⑲ $5\frac{2}{3}$

⑭ $3\frac{1}{4}$ ⑳ $6\frac{3}{4}$

⑮ $4\frac{2}{5}$ ㉑ $7\frac{1}{8}$

⑯ $5\frac{1}{5}$ ㉒ $4\frac{3}{7}$

⑰ $5\frac{1}{3}$ ㉓ $4\frac{7}{9}$

⑱ $2\frac{4}{5}$ ㉔ $6\frac{7}{10}$

On this page you will learn to collect like terms.

The expression $5a + 2a$ can be *simplified* to $7a$. This is because $5a + 2a$ means five a's plus two a's, which is equivalent to seven a's.

(It can also be remembered as '5 *apples* + 2 *apples* = 7 *apples*'.)

Similarly, the expression $7c - 3c$ can be simplified to $4c$.

The expression $10x + x$ can be thought of as $10x + 1x$ which can be simplified to $11x$.

Some expressions cannot be simplified.

The expression $7x + 2x$ consists of two terms, $7x$ and $2x$.

The expression $5x + 3y$ consists of two terms, $5x$ and $3y$.

$7x$ and $2x$ are called *like* terms.
$5x$ and $3y$ are called *unlike* terms.

An expression which is the sum or difference of two terms can only be simplified if the terms are *like* terms.

M

Collect like terms where possible.

1. $7x + 2x$
2. $4a + 5a$
3. $3a + 2a$
4. $9y + 2y$
5. $5x + 4x$
6. $5c - 2d$
7. $4x + 3x$

8. $9d + d$
9. $13y - y$
10. $6d - 4$
11. $6x + 3y$
12. $4h + 2h$
13. $7y - 5y$
14. $13x - 9x$

15. $7a + a$
16. $3a + b$
17. $4 - 2x$
18. $7d - 3d$
19. $10a - 4a$
20. $17t - 2t$
21. $19b + 3b$

22. $9c + 5c$
23. $5c - c$
24. $5c - 5$
25. $9a + a$
26. $9a + 9$
27. $11b - 11$
28. $11b - b$

E

For each question, collect like terms as much as possible.

1. $7a + 3b + 2a + 5b$
2. $9a + 2b + 3a + 2b$
3. $5c + 2c + 3d + 6d$
4. $6x + 3y + 2x + 9y$
5. $5x + 8y + 3y + 4x$
6. $5a + 6y - 2a - 4y$
7. $9x + 2b - 7x + 7b$

8. $6a + 3a - 2a + 5b$
9. $5c + 9d - 4d - 2d$
10. $2a + 12b + 6b - a$
11. $8y + 3 + y + 7$
12. $11a + 7 - a - 4$
13. $4x + 10 - x + 3$
14. $3a + 2b + 4c - a + 8c$

15. $5x + 6y + 2y - 3x + 2y + 2x$
16. $6x + 5x + 10y + 2y + 9x - 7y$
17. $5a + 3b + 6a + 9c - 2a + 5c$
18. $11a + 6b + 2b - 5a - 2a + 7b - 3b$
19. $12x + 6x + 19y - 3x - 7y + 4y - 2x$
20. $8a + 6b + 2b + 9c - 3a - 3b + 11c - 2b - 5c$

On these pages you will learn to use letters in place of numbers.

Ⓜ

The lengths of these shapes are in cm. Find the perimeter of each shape.

① 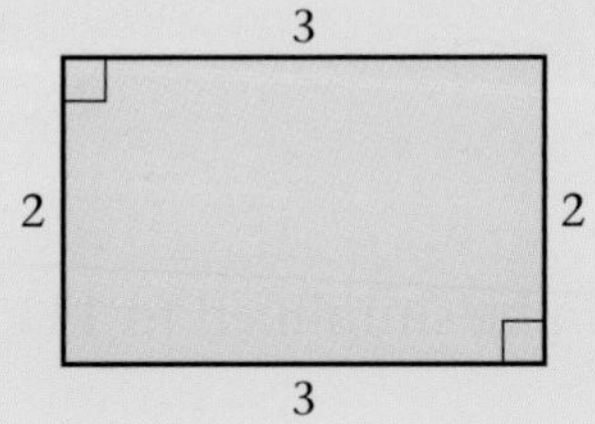 3 ... 2 ... 2 ... 3

② 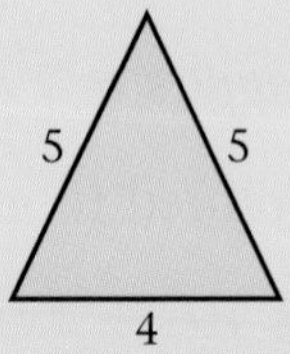 5 ... 5 ... 4

③ 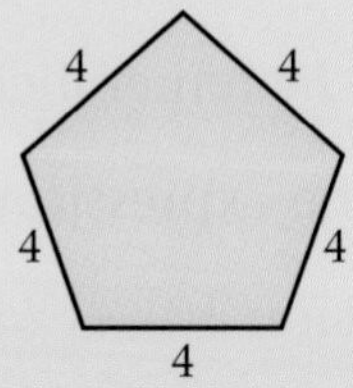 4 ... 4 ... 4 ... 4 ... 4

④ 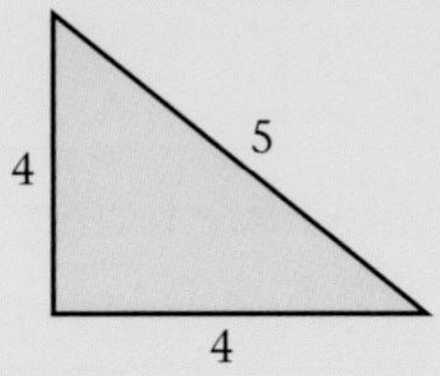 4 ... 5 ... 4

⑤ 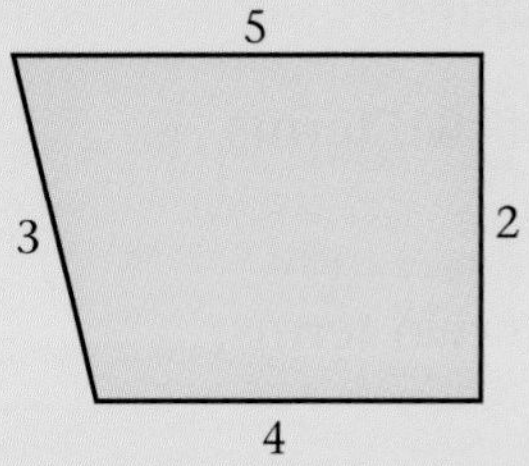 5 ... 3 ... 2 ... 4

⑥ 2 ... 2 ... 2 ... 2 ... 2 ... 2

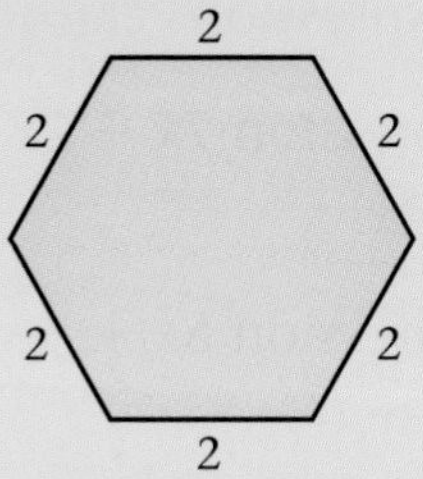

Find the perimeter of these shapes if *a* = 2 cm

⑦ 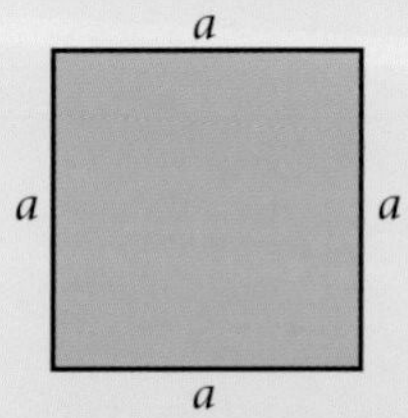 *a* ... *a* ... *a* ... *a*

⑧  *a* *a* ... *a* ... *a* ... *a* *a*

⑨ *a* *a* *a* ... *a* ... *a* *a* *a*

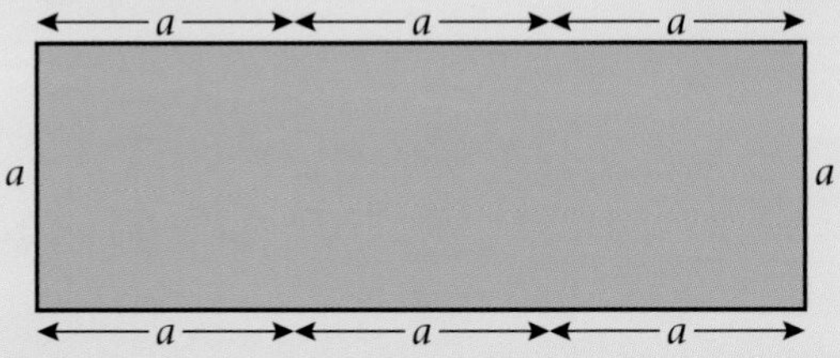

Find the perimeter of these shapes if *b* = 3 cm

⑩ 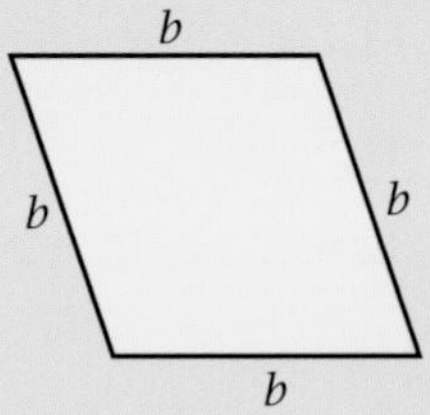 *b* ... *b* ... *b* ... *b*

⑪ 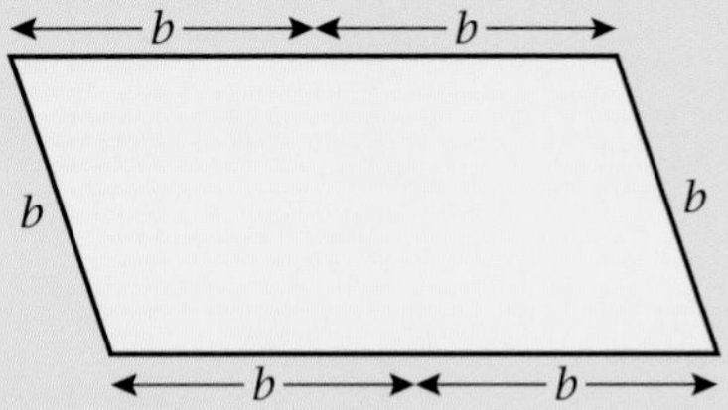 *b* *b* ... *b* ... *b* ... *b* *b*

⑫ *b* ... *b* ... *b*

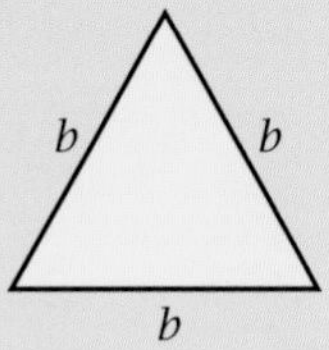

Find the perimeter of these shapes if *c* = 4 cm

⑬ 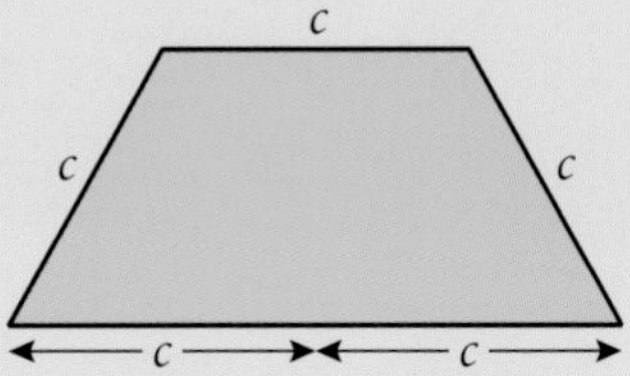 *c* ... *c* ... *c* ... *c* *c*

⑭ 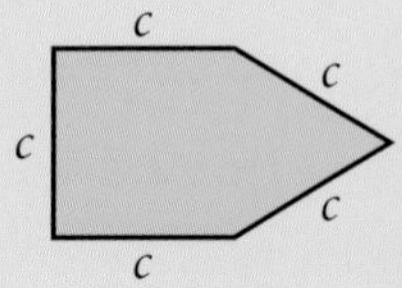 *c* ... *c* ... *c* ... *c*

⑮ *c* ... 2*c* ... *c* ... *c*

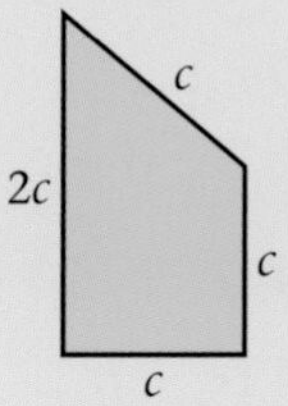

⑯ *c* ... *c* ... *c* ... *c* ... *c*

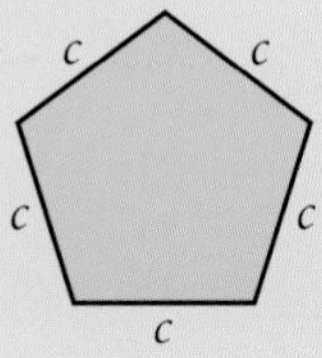

Find the perimeter of these shapes if $x = 5$ cm and $y = 4$ cm.

(17)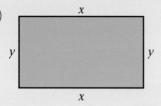

(18)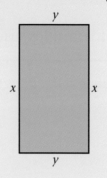

(19)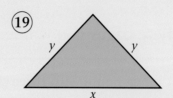

E

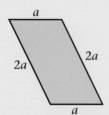

The perimeter of this shape is $a + b + a + b$
$$= 2a + 2b$$

Find the perimeter of each shape, using the letters a, b and c.

(1)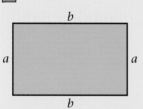

(2)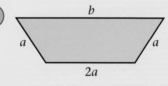

(3)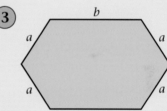

(4)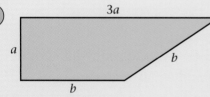

(5)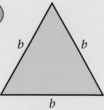

(6)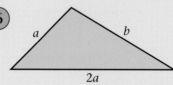

(7)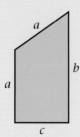

(8)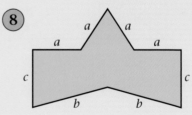

(9)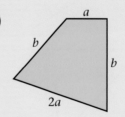

(10) For each shape in questions (1) to (9), find the perimeter if $a = 2$ cm, $b = 5$ cm and $c = 1$ cm.

(11) For each shape in questions (1) to (9), find the perimeter if $a = 3$ cm, $b = 7$ cm and $c = 2$ cm.

On these pages you will learn about triangles and other shapes.

- A plane figure with three sides and angles is a triangle.

- A triangle with three different sides and three different angles is a *scalene* triangle.

- A triangle with two sides the same length and two angles the same is an *isosceles* triangle.

- A triangle with three sides the same length and three equal angles is an *equilateral* triangle.

- A triangle which contains a right angle is a *right angled* triangle.

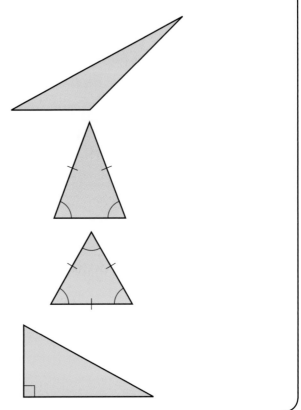

For each of the following triangles state whether it is scalene, isosceles, equilateral or right angled. (Lines of the same length are indicated by dashes and equal angles are marked.)

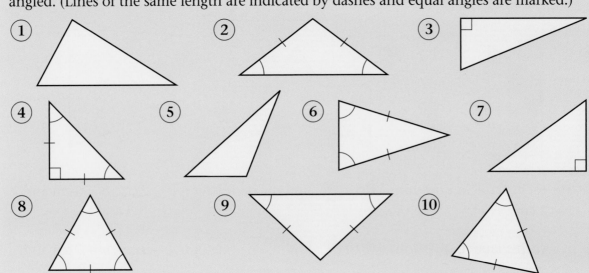

E

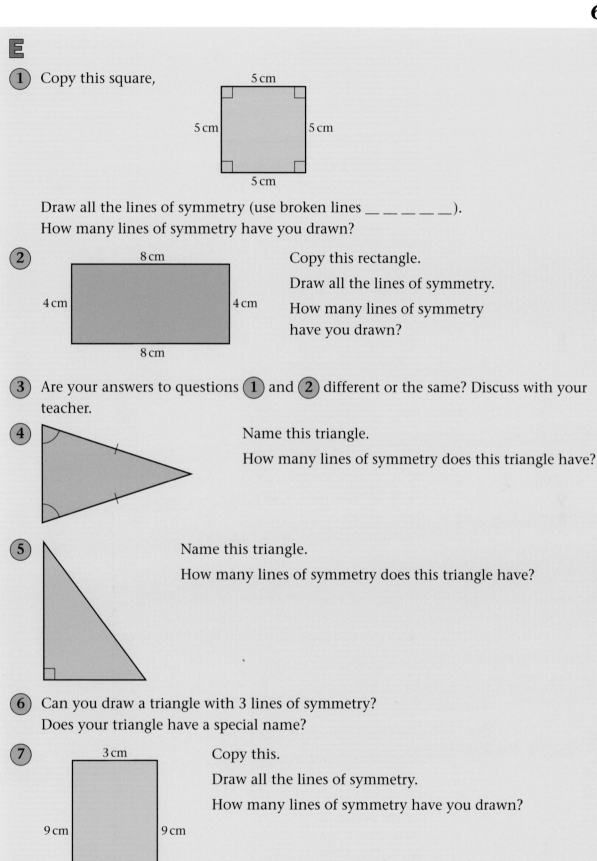

(1) Copy this square,

5 cm

5 cm   5 cm

5 cm

Draw all the lines of symmetry (use broken lines _ _ _ _ _).
How many lines of symmetry have you drawn?

(2) 8 cm

4 cm   4 cm

8 cm

Copy this rectangle.

Draw all the lines of symmetry.

How many lines of symmetry
have you drawn?

(3) Are your answers to questions (1) and (2) different or the same? Discuss with your teacher.

(4) Name this triangle.

How many lines of symmetry does this triangle have?

(5) Name this triangle.

How many lines of symmetry does this triangle have?

(6) Can you draw a triangle with 3 lines of symmetry?
Does your triangle have a special name?

(7) 3 cm

9 cm   9 cm

3 cm

Copy this.

Draw all the lines of symmetry.

How many lines of symmetry have you drawn?

On these pages you will learn to use co-ordinates to find the position of a point on a grid.

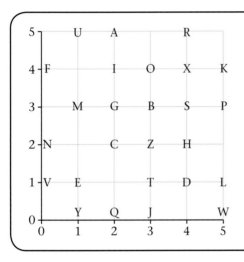

The position of a point on a grid is given by its co-ordinates. The across co-ordinate always comes first.

Examples

Point M is (1, 3).   Point Q is (2, 0).

Point T is (3, 1).   Point N is (0, 2).

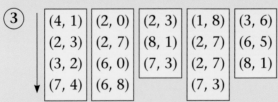

① Use the grid to spell out this message. Read across.

(5, 0)(4, 2)(1, 1)(0, 2) (1, 0)(3, 4)(1, 5) (0, 4)(2, 4)(0, 2)(4, 1) (2, 5)
(5, 3)(3, 4)(4, 3)(2, 4)(3, 1)(2, 4)(3, 4)(0, 2) (3, 4)(0, 2) (2, 5)
(2, 3)(4, 5)(2, 4)(4, 1) (2, 3)(3, 4) (2, 5)(2, 2)(4, 5)(3, 4)(4, 3)(4, 3)
(0, 4)(2, 4)(4, 5)(4, 3)(3, 1) (2, 5)(0, 2)(4, 1) (3, 1)(4, 2)(1, 1)(0, 2)
(2, 3)(3, 4) (1, 5)(5, 3).

② Write your name and the name of your school in co-ordinates.

Use the grid on the right to work out the message written in co-ordinates.
Each column spells out a word.

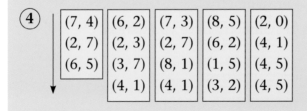

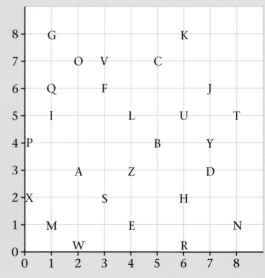

③

(4, 1)	(2, 0)	(2, 3)	(1, 8)	(3, 6)
(2, 3)	(2, 7)	(8, 1)	(2, 7)	(6, 5)
(3, 2)	(6, 0)	(7, 3)	(2, 7)	(8, 1)
(7, 4)	(6, 8)		(7, 3)	

④

(7, 4)	(6, 2)	(7, 3)	(8, 5)	(2, 0)
(2, 7)	(2, 3)	(2, 7)	(6, 2)	(4, 1)
(6, 5)	(3, 7)	(8, 1)	(1, 5)	(4, 5)
	(4, 1)	(4, 1)	(3, 2)	(4, 5)

⑤ Draw a 5 × 5 grid like the one shown below. Plot the points. Join them up in the order given. Use a different colour for each shape. What shapes have you drawn?

A	B	C	D
(1, 2)	(1, 0)	(3, 1)	(0, 4)
(1, 5)	(2, 3)	(3, 4)	(2, 4)
(4, 5)	(3, 0)	(5, 4)	(0, 1)
(4, 2)	(1, 0)	(5, 1)	(0, 4)
(1, 2)		(3, 1)	

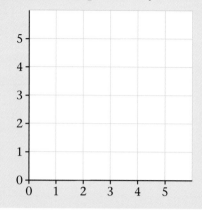

E

Draw a grid on squared paper like below.
Label across from 0 to 16 (horizontal axis).
Label up from 0 to 15 (vertical axis).

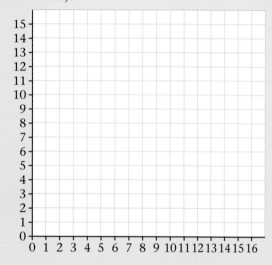

Plot the points below and join them up with a ruler in the order given.

(10, 8)	(10, 9)	(9, 10)	(8, 10)	(7, 10)	(6, 9)	(6, 8)
(7, 7)	(8, 7)	(9, 7)	(9, 6)	(10, 6)	(11, 6)	(11, 7)

ON THE SAME PICTURE plot the points below and join them up with a ruler in the order given.

DO NOT JOIN THE LAST POINT IN THE BOX ABOVE WITH THE FIRST POINT IN THE NEW BOX

(7, 5)	(8, 4)	(12, 4)	(14, 4)	(13, 7)	(16, 10)	(13, 11)
(12, 15)	(9, 13)	(7, 15)	(5, 12)	(2, 12)	(3, 9)	(1, 7)
(3, 6)	(3, 3)	(5, 4)	(6, 1)	(11, 1)	(12, 4)	

72

ON THE SAME PICTURE plot the points below and join them up with a ruler in the order given.

(9, 7)	(10, 8)	(11, 7)	(12, 7)	(13, 8)	(13, 9)
(12, 10)	(11, 10)	(10, 9)			

Draw a ⊕ around the points below, making

the circles touch like this

(5, 2)   (6, 2)   (7, 2)   (8, 2)   (9, 2)   (10, 2)   (11, 2)   (12, 2)

Draw a ● at $(8, 8\frac{1}{2})$ and a ● at $(12, 8\frac{1}{2})$

Who am I?   Colour me in?

On this page you will learn about acute, obtuse and reflex angles. You will also estimate the size of angles.

Remember – acute angles are less than 90°
– obtuse angles are between 90° and 180°
– reflex angles are greater than 180°

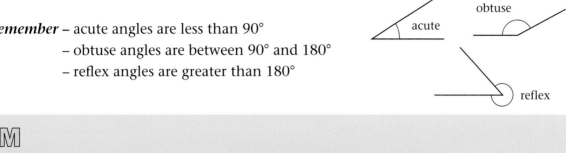

M

A Copy each angle and write down if it is acute, obtuse or reflex.

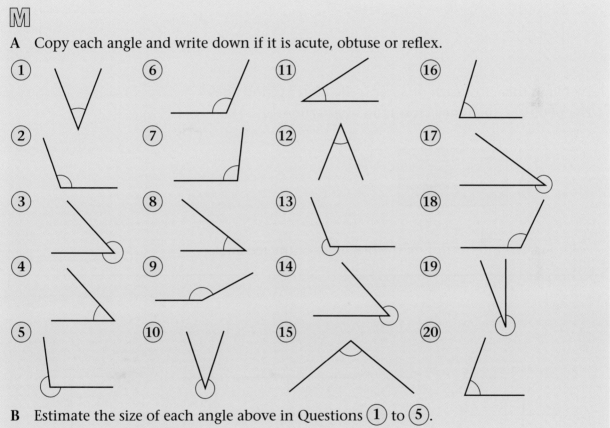

B Estimate the size of each angle above in Questions ① to ⑤.

E

Write down each angle and state if it is acute, obtuse or reflex.
① a) 45° b) 60° c) 150° d) 210°
e) 30° f) 240° g) 120° h) 80°
i) 110° j) 290° k) 75° l) 135°
m) 300° n) 12° o) 190° p) 107°
q) 10° r) 256° s) 350°

② Draw a diagram for each angle in question ① without using a protractor.
Write the size of the angle in the correct place on each diagram.

On these pages you will explore lines.

Parallel lines are lines that are the same distance apart for all their length. Railway lines are parallel lines.

Perpendicular lines cross or meet at right angles.

Two lines that cross each other are called intersecting lines. The point at which they cross is an intersection.

Point A is the intersection of the diagonals of the rectangle.

M

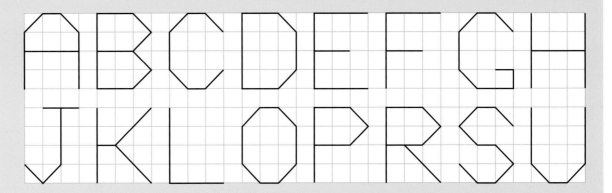

1. Use squared paper. Copy each of the letters above in a 3 × 4 grid. Show all the parallel lines with arrows or coloured pens or pencils, using a different colour for each pair of parallel lines in a letter. Show all the perpendicular lines by marking right angles.

⑱

Name this angle.

| acute | obtuse | reflex |

⑲

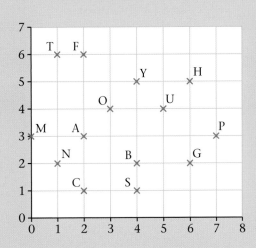

ABCD is a rectangle.
Write down one line which is **perpendicular** to the line DC.

⑳

Write down the letter at each of the following co-ordinates to make a word.

(4, 1)   (1, 6)   (3, 4)   (7, 3)

On this page you will explore the game of darts.

On a dartboard the outer ring doubles the score and the inner ring trebles the score. (Trebles means times by 3.)

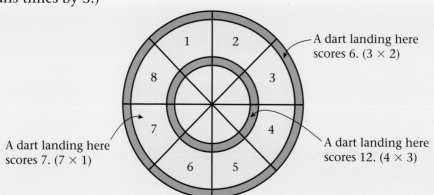

A dart landing here scores 6. (3 × 2)

A dart landing here scores 7. (7 × 1)

A dart landing here scores 12. (4 × 3)

Use <u>one</u> dart only in all the questions in this section.

1 What is the highest possible score?

2 Find two ways of scoring:
  a) 8   **c)** 4
  b) 2   **d)** 12.

3 Which number can be scored in three different ways?

4 Write down one way of scoring:
  a) 9   **d)** 10
  b) 14   **e)** 15
  c) 21   **f)** 16.

5 There are four numbers lower than 20 that you cannot score. What are they?

In this section use <u>two</u> darts only. Both darts must score.

6 What is the highest possible score with two darts?

7 Find two ways of scoring:
  a) 34   b) 39.

8 Find four ways of scoring:
  a) 36   **c)** 32
  b) 33   **d)** 29.

9 How can you score:
  a) 35   **c)** 38
  b) 37   **d)** 40?

10 Explore different ways of scoring these numbers.
  a) 17 b) 26 c) 31.

In this section use <u>three</u> darts only. All three darts must score.

11 What is the highest possible score using three darts?

12 How can you score 59?

13 There are three ways of scoring 58. What are they?

14 Which numbers in the 60s cannot be scored?

15 Explore different ways of scoring these numbers:
  a) 47 **b)** 51 **c)** 55.

16 Design a dartboard of your own. Investigate the scores that can be made on it, and the scores that cannot be made.

Multiplication Facts for 6 and 9

On this page you will practise the multiplication and division facts for 6 and 9.

M

Write the answers only.

1) 3×6
2) 10×6
3) 7×6
4) 9×6
5) 6×6
6) 2×6
7) 5×6
8) 0×6
9) 8×6
10) $36 \div 6$
11) $6 \div 6$
12) $60 \div 6$
13) $24 \div 6$
14) $48 \div 6$
15) $30 \div 6$
16) $54 \div 6$
17) $18 \div 6$
18) $42 \div 6$

Copy and complete.

19) $\boxed{} \times 6 = 18$
20) $\boxed{} \times 6 = 42$
21) $\boxed{} \times 6 = 24$
22) $\boxed{} \times 6 = 36$
23) $\boxed{} \times 6 = 0$
24) $\boxed{} \times 6 = 48$
25) $\boxed{} \times 6 = 30$
26) $\boxed{} \times 6 = 54$
27) $\boxed{} \div 6 = 5$
28) $\boxed{} \div 6 = 8$
29) $\boxed{} \div 6 = 10$
30) $\boxed{} \div 6 = 4$
31) $\boxed{} \div 6 = 7$
32) $\boxed{} \div 6 = 1$
33) $\boxed{} \div 6 = 9$
34) $\boxed{} \div 6 = 6$

E

Write the answers only.

1) 4×9
2) 8×9
3) 1×9
4) 10×9
5) 0×9
6) 6×9
7) 9×9
8) 5×9
9) 7×9
10) $27 \div 9$
11) $45 \div 9$
12) $81 \div 9$
13) $54 \div 9$
14) $18 \div 9$
15) $36 \div 9$
16) $63 \div 9$
17) $90 \div 9$
18) $72 \div 9$

Copy and complete.

19) $\boxed{} \times 9 = 54$
20) $\boxed{} \times 9 = 36$
21) $\boxed{} \times 9 = 81$
22) $\boxed{} \times 9 = 90$
23) $\boxed{} \times 9 = 27$
24) $\boxed{} \times 9 = 72$
25) $\boxed{} \times 9 = 45$
26) $\boxed{} \times 9 = 63$
27) $\boxed{} \div 9 = 4$
28) $\boxed{} \div 9 = 10$
29) $\boxed{} \div 9 = 8$
30) $\boxed{} \div 9 = 3$
31) $\boxed{} \div 9 = 7$
32) $\boxed{} \div 9 = 1$
33) $\boxed{} \div 9 = 6$
34) $\boxed{} \div 9 = 9$

On this page you will practise the multiplication and division facts for 7 and 8.

Ⓜ

Write the answers only.

① 5×7
② 2×7
③ 4×7
④ 0×7
⑤ 9×7
⑥ 7×7
⑦ 8×7
⑧ 6×7
⑨ 10×7

⑩ $21 \div 7$
⑪ $70 \div 7$
⑫ $56 \div 7$
⑬ $14 \div 7$
⑭ $42 \div 7$
⑮ $35 \div 7$
⑯ $63 \div 7$
⑰ $28 \div 7$
⑱ $49 \div 7$

Copy and complete.

⑲ $\square \times 7 = 14$
⑳ $\square \times 7 = 35$
㉑ $\square \times 7 = 56$
㉒ $\square \times 7 = 21$

㉓ $\square \times 7 = 42$
㉔ $\square \times 7 = 28$
㉕ $\square \times 7 = 63$
㉖ $\square \times 7 = 49$

㉗ $\square \div 7 = 3$
㉘ $\square \div 7 = 7$
㉙ $\square \div 7 = 2$
㉚ $\square \div 7 = 5$

㉛ $\square \div 7 = 9$
㉜ $\square \div 7 = 6$
㉝ $\square \div 7 = 1$
㉞ $\square \div 7 = 8$

Ⓔ

Write the answers only.

① 3×8
② 10×8
③ 6×8
④ 0×8
⑤ 9×8
⑥ 4×8
⑦ 7×8
⑧ 1×8
⑨ 8×8

⑩ $40 \div 8$
⑪ $80 \div 8$
⑫ $24 \div 8$
⑬ $72 \div 8$
⑭ $48 \div 8$
⑮ $8 \div 8$
⑯ $64 \div 8$
⑰ $32 \div 8$
⑱ $56 \div 8$

Copy and complete.

⑲ $\square \times 8 = 40$
⑳ $\square \times 8 = 24$
㉑ $\square \times 8 = 48$
㉒ $\square \times 8 = 16$

㉓ $\square \times 8 = 72$
㉔ $\square \times 8 = 56$
㉕ $\square \times 8 = 32$
㉖ $\square \times 8 = 64$

㉗ $\square \div 8 = 3$
㉘ $\square \div 8 = 7$
㉙ $\square \div 8 = 1$
㉚ $\square \div 8 = 4$

㉛ $\square \div 8 = 8$
㉜ $\square \div 8 = 6$
㉝ $\square \div 8 = 5$
㉞ $\square \div 8 = 9$

On this page you will learn to count on and back in 1s, 10s and 100s.

M

Count on in 10s.
1. 50 from 282
2. 80 from 467
3. 60 from 741
4. 70 from 955

Count back in 1s.
5. 5 from 357
6. 6 from 274
7. 7 from 638
8. 8 from 495

Count on in 100s.
9. 400 from 1812
10. 700 from 1764
11. 500 from 3635
12. 800 from 2790

Count back in 10s.
13. 40 from 523
14. 50 from 130
15. 60 from 952
16. 80 from 726

Count on in 1000s.
17. 3000 from 1271
18. 5000 from 3952
19. 4000 from 2503
20. 7000 from 3487

Count back in 100s.
21. 300 from 2165
22. 600 from 3587
23. 500 from 1240
24. 700 from 7391

Add 10 to:
25. 538
26. 279
27. 165
28. 421.

Add 100 to:
29. 4210
30. 3587
31. 2941
32. 5756

Add 1000 to:
33. 2491
34. 6580
35. 374
36. 7900

Take 10 from:
37. 762
38. 413
39. 359
40. 806

E

Copy and complete the calculation squares.

1.

+	100	10	1	100
1697	1797			
399				
2914		2924		
4979				

2.

−	10	100	1000	1
3210		3110		
1398				
2107				2106
4052				

Add 30 to:
3. 365
4. 1258
5. 2381

Start at 479.
15. +1
16. +100
17. +1000

Add 200 to:
6. 869
7. 1437
8. 2917

Start at 1203.
18. −100
19. −10
20. −1000.

Take 20 from:
9. 1367
10. 814
11. 1605

Start at 5309.
21. +10
22. +1
23. +1000.

Take 300 from:
12. 5416
13. 1230
14. 7001

Start at 2999.
24. +1
25. +10
26. +100.

On these pages you will learn to use the symbols $<$, $>$ and $=$ and to put numbers into order.

$>$ means 'is greater than'.
$<$ means 'is less than'.
$=$ means 'is equal to'.

Example
2581   2158   21158

Put these numbers in order with the largest first.

The 2 in 21158 has a value of 20000 and is the highest value digit.

The 2s in 2581 and 2158 both have a value of 2000.

The 5 in 2581 is the second digit with the highest value in that pair of numbers.

Therefore the order is:
21158   2581   2158.

Example
Find the number half way between 6200 and 6800.

Find the difference between the numbers.
$6800 - 6200 = 600$

Work out half the difference.
$600 \div 2 = 300$

Add half the difference to the lower number.
$6200 + 300 = 6500$

M

Put these sets of numbers in order starting with the smallest.

1. 382   283   823   238
2. 714   417   174   471
3. 325   532   523   352
4. 649   469   496   694

Find the number that is halfway on each of these number lines.

5. 210 _____ 220

6. 95 _____ 105

7. 500 _____ 600

8. 300 _____ 310

Answer 'True' or 'False'.

9. $62 > 26$
10. $308 < 380$
11. $10 \times 8 > 3 \times 30$
12. Half of $100 < 5 \times 10$

Copy and complete by putting $<$, $>$ or $=$ in the box.

13. $7 \times 2 \ \square \ 2 \times 5$
14. $8 \times 3 \ \square \ 4 \times 6$
15. $6 \times 4 \ \square \ 5 \times 5$

(16) $3 \times 6 \ \square \ 9 \times 2$

(17) $5 \times 7 \ \square \ 6 \times 6$

(18) $10 \times 6 \ \square \ 15 \times 3$

(19) $8 \times 4 \ \square \ 7 \times 5$

(20) $7 \times 3 \ \square \ 5 \times 4$

(21) $5 \times 8 \ \square \ 10 \times 4$

(22) $6 \times 3 \ \square \ 4 \times 5$

(23) $10 \times 9 \ \square \ 45 \times 2$

(24) $9 \times 4 \ \square \ 5 \times 7$

Put these numbers in order, starting with the largest.

(25) 2635   3256   2536   3526

(26) 1984   1849   1498   4189

(27) 6472   7462   6724   7246

(28) 3748   3874   3784   3478

(29) 1546   1654   1456   1465

(30) 3187   3781   3871   3817

Find the number that is halfway on each of these number lines.

(31) 1300 ————|———— 1310

(32) 550 ————|———— 600

(33) 2000 ————|———— 2100

(34) 150 ————|———— 250

(35) 1360 ————|———— 1400

(36) 1900 ————|———— 2000

E

Copy and complete by putting $<$, $>$ or $=$ in the box.

(1) $7 \times 6 \ \square \ 8 \times 5$

(2) $9 \times 6 \ \square \ 14 \times 4$

(3) $6 \times 9 \ \square \ 27 \times 2$

(4) $7 \times 8 \ \square \ 3 \times 18$

(5) $8 \times 6 \ \square \ 4 \times 12$

(6) $8 \times 9 \ \square \ 3 \times 25$

(7) $9 \times 9 \ \square \ 4 \times 20$

(8) $6 \times 8 \ \square \ 7 \times 7$

(9) $6 \times 7 \ \square \ 14 \times 3$

(10) $7 \times 7 \ \square \ 25 \times 2$

(11) $9 \times 8 \ \square \ 3 \times 24$

(12) $8 \times 7 \ \square \ 11 \times 5$

(13) Use these digits once each.
Make two 3-digit numbers which give:

a) the largest possible total.
b) the smallest possible total.
c) the largest possible difference.
d) the smallest possible difference.

Work out the number that is halfway between these numbers.

(14) 3460 ⟵⟶ 3660

(15) 2000 ⟵⟶ 2500

(16) 4530 ⟵⟶ 4610

(17) 19 500 ⟵⟶ 21 500

(18) 950 ⟵⟶ 1050

(19) 2095 ⟵⟶ 2125

(29) 1440 ⟵⟶ 1500

(21) 17 280 ⟵⟶ 17 290

On these pages you will learn about multiples.

> A multiple of 6 is any number in the six times table.
> This could be 6 or 12 or 18 or 24 or any other number in the six times table.

Ⓜ

Copy the grids below and put a ring around all the multiples of the number shown.

① Multiples of 6.

1	2	3	4	5	6	7	8	9	10
11	12	13	14	15	16	17	18	19	20
21	22	23	24	25	26	27	28	29	30
31	32	33	34	35	36	37	38	39	40
41	42	43	44	45	46	47	48	49	50
51	52	53	54	55	56	57	58	59	60
61	62	63	64	65	66	67	68	69	70
71	72	73	74	75	76	77	78	79	80
81	82	83	84	85	86	87	88	89	90
91	92	93	94	95	96	97	98	99	100

④ Multiples of 7.

1	2	3	4	5	6				
7	8	9	10	11	12				
13	14	15	16	17	18				
19	20	21	22	23	24	25	26	27	28
29	30	31	32	33	34	35	36	37	38
39	40	41	42	43	44	45	46	47	48

② Multiples of 9.

1	2	3	4	5	6	7	8	9	10
11	12	13	14	15	16	17	18	19	20
21	22	23	24	25	26	27	28	29	30
31	32	33	34	35	36	37	38	39	40
41	42	43	44	45	46	47	48	49	50
51	52	53	54	55	56	57	58	59	60
61	62	63	64	65	66	67	68	69	70
71	72	73	74	75	76	77	78	79	80
81	82	83	84	85	86	87	88	89	90
91	92	93	94	95	96	97	98	99	100

⑤ Multiples of 5.

1	2	3	4	5	6	7	8	9
10	11	12	13	14	15	16	17	18
19	20	21	22	23	24	25	26	27
28	29	30	31	32	33	34	35	36

③ Multiples of 8.

1	2	3	4	5	6	7	8	9	10
11	12	13	14	15	16	17	18	19	20
21	22	23	24	25	26	27	28	29	30
31	32	33	34	35	36	37	38	39	40
41	42	43	44	45	46	47	48	49	50
51	52	53	54	55	56	57	58	59	60
61	62	63	64	65	66	67	68	69	70
71	72	73	74	75	76	77	78	79	80
81	82	83	84	85	86	87	88	89	90
91	92	93	94	95	96	97	98	99	100

⑥ Multiples of 4.

1	2	3	4	5	6				
7	8	9	10	11	12				
13	14	15	16	17	18				
19	20	21	22	23	24	25	26	27	28
29	30	31	32	33	34	35	36	37	38
39	40	41	42	43	44	45	46	47	48

7 Multiples of 3.

1	2	3	4	5	6	7	8	9	10
11	12	13	14	15	16	17	18	19	20
21	22	23	24	25	26	27	28	29	30
31	32	33	34	35	36	37	38	39	40
41	42	43	44	45	46	47	48	49	50
51	52	53	54	55	56	57	58	59	60
61	62	63	64	65	66	67	68	69	70
71	72	73	74	75	76	77	78	79	80
81	82	83	84	85	86	87	88	89	90
91	92	93	94	95	96	97	98	99	100

9 Multiples of 8.

		2	4				
	6	8	10	12			
14	16	18	20	22	24		
26	28	30	32	34	36	38	40
	42	44	46	48	50	52	
		54	56	58	60		
		62	64				

8 Multiples of 6.

1	2	3	4	5	6	7	8	9	10
11	12	13	14	15	16	17	18	19	20
21	22	23	24	25	26	27	28	29	30
31	32	33	34	35	36	37	38	39	40
41	42	43	44	45	46	47	48	49	50
51	52	53	54	55	56	57	58	59	60
61	62	63	64	65	66	67	68	69	70
71	72	73	74	75	76	77	78	79	80
81	82	83	84	85	86	87	88	89	90
91	92	93	94	95	96	97	98	99	100

10 Multiples of 7.

3	6	9	12	15	18
					21
39	36	33	30	27	24
42					
45	48	51	54	57	60

E

Copy and colour in the multiples of 7.

1	67	27	82	8	58	43	83	51	3
81	70	42	49	56	21	35	28	73	13
12	44	84	65	66	85	63	74	39	6
16	76	37	8	40	56	75	18	59	36
5	13	29	22	14	33	60	64	45	6
20	78	52	56	10	54	48	19	30	12
33	41	77	18	31	11	69	23	71	10
27	24	21	46	72	15	57	50	32	20
17	25	7	55	38	61	34	22	79	25
4	68	62	53	9	26	26	80	47	2

What pattern do you see?

Copy and colour in the multiples of 6.

18	1	52	17	40	55	34	60	3	6
54	51	58	19	53	11	63	48	29	30
42	57	65	23	59	49	61	42	61	54
64	30	62	43	14	63	66	25	51	12
7	66	45	62	10	59	54	64	5	48
28	56	12	58	38	6	44	31	57	24
13	55	36	50	33	30	65	37	15	42
21	39	32	48	50	24	53	27	47	36
26	52	46	20	12	41	56	22	9	18
65	2	35	46	8	67	16	49	4	47

On these pages you will learn how to find all the factors of a number.

A factor is a number which divides exactly into another number. (There is no remainder.)

Example

How many **different** rectangles or squares can you make from 18 small squares?

A long thin rectangle is made of 18 small squares as shown.

18

We can make another rectangle with two rows of 9 small squares.

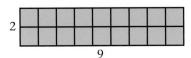

9

And yet another can be made with three rows of 6 small squares.

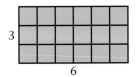

6

Can we make rectangles with 4 rows or 5 rows?

We cannot because 4 and 5 do not divide into 18.

We stop now because we have already used 6 in an earlier rectangle.

The length and width numbers on each rectangle are *factors* of 18.

The factors of 18 are 1 and 18, 2 and 9, 3 and 6.

Ⓜ

Draw all the **different** rectangles you can make from

① 8 small squares

② 4 small squares

③ 36 small squares

④ 32 small squares

⑤ 16 small squares

⑥ 12 small squares

⑦ 20 small squares

⑧ 42 small squares

⑨ 21 small squares

⑩ 13 small squares

Remember:
A square is
a rectangle

Count the number of small squares in the following shapes and use them all to make a rectangle or a square in as many ways as you can.

(Can you tell in advance if you can make more than one rectangle from each of these shapes?)

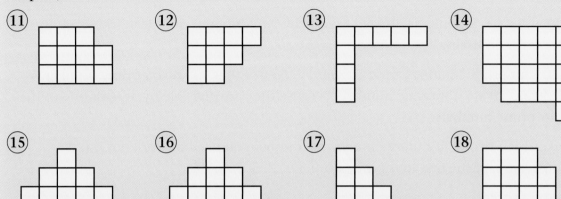

E

We can find all the factors of a number without drawing rectangles.
To find the factors of 18.

Start with 1 and 18.
Next try to divide 18 by 2. It goes 9 times. So 2 and 9 are factors.
Next try to divide 18 by 3. It goes 6 times. So 3 and 6 are factors.
Try to divide by 4. Not possible.
Try to divide by 5. Not possible.
We have already used 6 so stop now.

So the factors of 18 are 1 and 18, 2 and 9, 3 and 6.
These have been written as pairs of factors.
Find all the pairs of factors of the following:

(1) 6 (There are 2 pairs)

(5) 8 (There are 2 pairs)

(2) 12 (There are 3 pairs)

(6) 14 (There are 2 pairs)

(3) 15 (There are 2 pairs)

(7) 28 (There are 3 pairs)

(4) 20 (There are 3 pairs)

(8) 25 (There are 2 pairs)

(9) 16

(12) 10

(15) 13

(18) 42

(10) 40

(13) 22

(16) 11

(19) 45

(11) 36

(14) 9

(17) 35

(20) 72

On this page you will learn to recognise prime numbers.

A prime number can only be divided exactly by two different numbers: (these are the number one and itself).

The first four prime numbers are 2, 3, 5 and 7. Notice that 1 is **not** a prime number. 4, 6, 8, 9 and 10 are not prime numbers because they are divisible by at least one of the first four prime numbers.

To find out if a two-digit number is a prime number you need to work out if it is divisible by one of the first four prime numbers, 2, 3, 5 and 7.

Examples

28 is divisible by 7.   28 is not a prime number.
29 is not divisible by 2, 3, 5 or 7.   29 is a prime number.
30 is divisible by 2, 3 and 5.   30 is not a prime number.
31 is not divisible by 2, 3, 5 or 7.   31 is a prime number.

Write down the prime number in each group.

① 7 8 9   ⑤ 47 48 49

② 16 17 18   ⑥ 57 58 59

③ 21 22 23   ⑦ 66 67 68

④ 30 31 32   ⑧ 73 74 75

⑨ Find all the prime numbers below 50. There are 15. (Remember, 1 is not a prime number.)

⑩ Find the next prime number after 37.

E

Write down the two numbers in each group which are not prime numbers.

① 1 11 21 31

② 40 41 42 43

③ 33 43 53 63

④ 47 57 67 77

⑤ 51 61 71 81

⑥ 67 77 87 97

Write down the next prime number after:

⑦ 30   ⑨ 50

⑧ 45   ⑩ 75

⑪ Find all the prime numbers below 100. There are 25.

On this page you will learn a standard written method for multiplication.

Examples

```
        24              37              236
   ×     8         ×     4         ×      7
      ─────           ─────           ──────
      1 9 2           1 4 8           1 6 5 2
        3               2               2 4
```

Ⓜ

Work out.

① 67
  × 2

② 26
  × 4

③ 32
  × 6

④ 41
  × 7

⑤ 39
  × 5

⑥ 59
  × 3

⑦ 83
  × 2

⑧ 28
  × 5

⑨ 14
  × 8

⑩ 37
  × 4

Now do these..

⑪ 46
  × 4

⑫ 73
  × 5

⑬ 25
  × 8

⑭ 19
  × 9

⑮ 58
  × 3

⑯ 34
  × 6

⑰ 53
  × 7

⑱ 26
  × 8

⑲ 64
  × 5

⑳ 39
  × 4

Ⓔ

Work out.

① 368
  × 5

② 629
  × 4

③ 137
  × 4

④ 245
  × 7

⑤ 157
  × 6

⑥ 325
  × 9

⑦ 168
  × 7

⑧ 598
  × 3

⑨ 436
  × 8

⑩ 158
  × 9

Set out correctly and then work out.

⑪ 318 × 6

⑫ 182 × 8

⑬ 473 × 5

⑭ 329 × 7

⑮ 246 × 9

⑯ 397 × 8

⑰ A train ticket costs £7. How much will 315 tickets cost?

On this page you will practise long multiplication. (2 digit by 2 digit numbers)

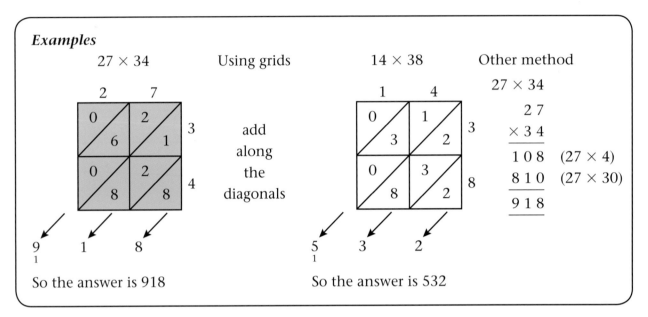

Examples

27 × 34   Using grids   14 × 38   Other method

add
along
the
diagonals

So the answer is 918   So the answer is 532

27 × 34

  2 7
× 3 4
─────
1 0 8   (27 × 4)
8 1 0   (27 × 30)
─────
9 1 8

M

Work out.

(1)   26
     × 14

(2)   14
     × 15

(3)   23
     × 16

(4)   31
     × 22

(5) 24 × 13

(6) 32 × 21

(7) 25 × 16

(8) 34 × 23

(9) 16 × 35

(10) 42 × 32

(11) A pair of trainers
     cost £18.
     How much do
     you pay for
     52 pairs of trainers?

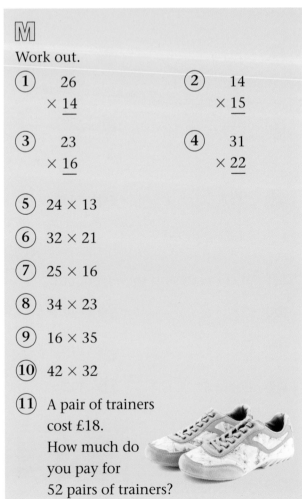

E

Work out.

(1)   68
     × 34

(2)   73
     × 18

(3)   92
     × 27

(4)   65
     × 46

(5)   78
     × 52

(8)   75
     × 29

(6)   48
     × 37

(9)   59
     × 34

(7)   39
     × 16

(10)   68
     × 25

(11) A solid fuel stove uses 25 kg of coal
     per day. How much does it use in
     16 days?

(12) There are 52 playing cards in a `deck'.
     How many cards are there in 24 decks?

Remainders

On this page you will learn to divide and to give a remainder.

Examples

$26 \div 5 = 5$ remainder 1

$37 \div 10 = 3$ remainder 7

M

Copy and complete.

1. $17 \div 4 = 4$ rem. ☐
2. $16 \div 5 = 3$ rem. ☐
3. $23 \div 2 = 11$ rem. ☐
4. $85 \div 10 = 8$ rem. ☐
5. $33 \div 5 = 6$ rem. ☐
6. $29 \div 4 = 7$ rem. ☐
7. $42 \div 5 = 8$ rem. ☐
8. $63 \div 10 = 6$ rem. ☐
9. $26 \div 3 = 8$ rem. ☐

10. How many packets of 10 can be made from 76 felt tip pens? How many pens are left over?

11. Five friends share 32 marbles. How many does each person get? How many are left over?

Work out and give the remainder as a whole number.

12. $21 \div 2$
13. $17 \div 3$
14. $37 \div 4$
15. $113 \div 10$
16. $69 \div 5$
17. $37 \div 2$
17. $28 \div 3$
18. $23 \div 4$
20. $37 \div 5$
21. $17 \div 4$

E

Work out

1. $154 \div 6$
2. $248 \div 7$
3. $221 \div 8$
4. $313 \div 9$
5. $199 \div 6$
6. $323 \div 7$
7. $378 \div 8$
8. $388 \div 9$
9. $265 \div 6$
10. $401 \div 7$
11. $437 \div 8$
12. $591 \div 9$
13. $347 \div 6$
14. $513 \div 7$
15. $516 \div 8$
16. $700 \div 9$

17. There are eight rolls in a packet. How many packets can be made from 312 rolls?

18. Footballs cost £7. How many can a school buy for £196?

19. Six boxes contain 216 apples altogether. How many apples are there in one box?

20. Six presents cost £45. Each present costs the same amount. How much does each present cost?

21. There are 468 bricks arranged in nine equal piles. How many bricks are in each pile?

On this page you will practise long multiplication (3 digit by 2 digit numbers).

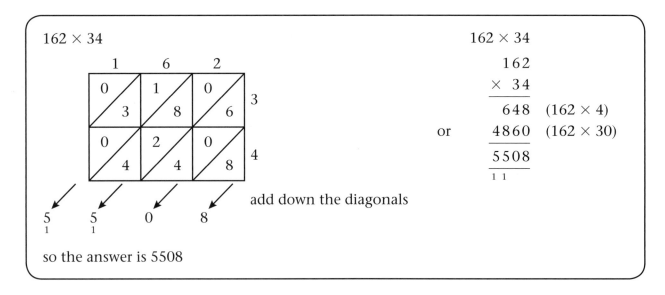

162 × 34

add down the diagonals

5 5 0 8
1 1

so the answer is 5508

162 × 34

```
      162
    ×  34
     ————
      648   (162 × 4)
or   4860   (162 × 30)
     ————
     5508
     ————
      1 1
```

Ⓜ

Work out.

①   132
    × 14

②   114
    × 13

③   244
    × 35

④   324
    × 14

⑤ 312 × 24

⑥ 205 × 31

⑦ 411 × 23

⑧ 521 × 32

⑨ 345 × 43

⑩ 431 × 55

⑪ A meal in a restaurant costs £24 per head. How much does it cost for 234 people?

Ⓔ

Copy and complete.

① 171 × 36   ⑤ 464 × 18

② 365 × 38   ⑥ 259 × 42

③ 247 × 19   ⑦ 373 × 29

④ 192 × 45   ⑧ 416 × 57

⑨ A party of 237 football supporters travel to an away game by train. Each ticket costs £48. What is the total cost of the tickets?

⑩ Angie earns £197 each week. How much does she earn in a year?

⑪ Each can weighs 364 g. What is the weight of 36 cans in kilograms?

⑫ Suppose you save 25 pence for every day you attend school (190 days). How much money will you have saved?

On this page you will learn how to divide numbers including decimals.

> **Examples:**
>
> $$4\overline{)8\ 5^12} = 2\ 1\ 3$$ $$5\overline{)7^25} = 1\ 5$$ $$3\overline{)4\ .^12} = 1\cdot 4$$ $$6\overline{)9\ .^30} = 1\cdot 5$$

Ⓜ

Work out.

(1) $3\overline{)36}$ (4) $4\overline{)208}$ (7) $2\overline{)164}$ (10) $6\overline{)306}$ (13) $2\overline{)10\cdot8}$ (16) $5\overline{)31\cdot5}$

(2) $4\overline{)28}$ (5) $2\overline{)106}$ (8) $3\overline{)126}$ (11) $6\overline{)114}$ (14) $3\overline{)31\cdot5}$ (17) $5\overline{)14\cdot5}$

(3) $5\overline{)45}$ (6) $7\overline{)56}$ (9) $4\overline{)140}$ (12) $2\overline{)14\cdot6}$ (15) $2\overline{)21\cdot6}$ (18) $6\overline{)42\cdot6}$

Money questions.

(19) £18·60 ÷ 3   (22) £40·80 ÷ 4   (25) £20·25 ÷ 5   (28) £5·25 ÷ 5

(20) £22 ÷ 5   (23) £6·36 ÷ 3   (26) £11 ÷ 5   (29) £14·20 ÷ 4

(21) £18·66 ÷ 6   (24) £10·50 ÷ 7   (27) £4·20 ÷ 8   (30) £19·50 ÷ 5

Ⓔ

(1) $3\overline{)4155}$ (4) $8\overline{)5608}$ (7) $6\overline{)9018}$ (10) $8\overline{)2336}$ (13) $2\overline{)8\cdot3}$ (16) $4\overline{)18\cdot2}$

(2) $4\overline{)408}$ (5) $9\overline{)4509}$ (8) $9\overline{)2817}$ (11) $9\overline{)4545}$ (14) $2\overline{)42\cdot1}$ (17) $5\overline{)76\cdot1}$

(3) $5\overline{)6625}$ (6) $7\overline{)4410}$ (9) $8\overline{)4520}$ (12) $7\overline{)2037}$ (15) $3\overline{)76\cdot2}$ (18) $5\overline{)113\cdot4}$

(19) Four children share £25·60 equally between them.
How much does each child receive?

(20) A bill of £84·24 is shared equally by 6 people.
How much should each person pay?

(21) Three brothers agree to pay equal shares for their mother's birthday present. How much should each one pay if the present costs £55·50?

(22) The first prize in a netball competition was £75·60 and was shared by the six members of the team. How much did each player win?

(23) Five members of a basketball team shared a bill of £80·50 for a broken window in the Sports Hall. How much does each person pay?

On these pages you will learn to make sensible decisions about rounding up or down after division.

Examples

- Tickets cost £5.
  I have £34.
  How many tickets can I buy?
  34 ÷ 5 = 6 remainder 4.
  Answer: I can buy 6 tickets.

- A car can carry 5 people.
  34 people need transport.
  How many cars are needed?
  34 ÷ 5 = 6 remainder 4.
  Answer: 7 cars are needed.

- A relay team needs 4 runners.
  There are 22 runners.
  How many teams can be made?
  22 ÷ 4 = 5 remainder 2
  Answer: 5 teams can be made.

- 4 children sit at each table.
  There are 22 children.
  How many tables are needed?
  22 ÷ 4 = 5 remainder 2
  Answer: 6 tables are needed.

M

Write the answers only.

1. Two children can sit at each table.
   There are 17 children.
   How many tables are needed?

2. There are 28 children at a football club.
   How many 5-a-side teams can be made?

3. Ten children can sit on a bench. There are 68 children.
   How many benches are needed?

4. One chocolate costs 10p.
   I have 24p.
   How many chocolates can I buy?

5. Dean saves £2 every week.
   How long will it take him to save £11?

6. There are 15 children at a tennis club.
   How many pairs of children can be made?

7. A baker makes 47 cakes.
   Five cakes can fit into one box.
   How many boxes are needed?

8. A florist has 93 flowers. A bunch of flowers has ten flowers.
   How many bunches can she make?

⑨ Zoe has 108 pens.
Each packet holds 10 pens.
How many packets does she need?

⑩ Derek can saw 3 boards from each
plank. How many planks are needed
to saw 25 boards?

⑪ A tennis coach has 42 tennis balls.
Each box holds four balls.
How many boxes does he need?

⑫ There are 30 children in a P.E.
lesson. How many teams of four can
be made?

⑬ There are 27 children in a class.
Six children can sit at each table.
How many tables are needed?

⑭ Cans of drink are sold in packs of
four. There are 26 cans.
How many packs of four can be
made?

E

① 230 children are going on a trip.
Each coach can carry 50 children.
How many coaches are needed?

② Rolls are sold in packets of 8.
A baker has 46 rolls.
How many packets can he make?

③ The 190 pupils in a school need a
Maths exercise book. The books are
sold in packs of 20.
How many packs are needed?

④ A farmer has 46 eggs.
A box holds 6 eggs.
How many boxes can be filled?

⑤ 210 tickets have been sold for a
school concert.
25 chairs make one row.
How many rows of chairs are
needed?

⑥ 40 children want to play netball.
Each team has 7 players.
How many teams can be made?

⑦ There are 148 empty bottles.
Each crate holds 20 bottles.
How many crates are needed?

⑧ Kerry has £50.
Skate boards cost £9 each.
How many skate boards can she buy?

⑨ The 28 children in a class need
rubbers. Each box holds 8 rubbers.
How many boxes does the teacher
need to collect?

On these pages you will learn to round a number to the nearest 10 or 100.

ROUNDING TO THE NEAREST 10
Look at the units column.
5 or more, round up.
Less than 5, round down.

Examples
39 rounds to 40
34 rounds to 30
45 rounds to 50

ROUNDING TO THE NEAREST 100
Look at the tens and units columns.
50 or more, round up.
Less than 50, round down.

Examples
462 rounds to 500
448 rounds to 400
750 rounds to 800

ROUNDING DECIMALS TO THE
NEAREST WHOLE NUMBER
Look at the tenths column.
5 or more, round up.
Less than 5, round down.

Examples
3·5 rounds to 4
5·49 rounds to 5
£2·70 rounds to £3

Ⓜ

Round to the nearest 10.

① 84	⑤ 13	⑨ 17
② 37	⑥ 25	⑩ 33
③ 29	⑦ 61	⑪ 65
④ 72	⑧ 48	⑫ 98

Round to the nearest 100.

⑬ 130	⑰ 620	㉑ 952
⑭ 460	⑱ 850	㉒ 495
⑮ 380	⑲ 573	㉓ 847
⑯ 710	⑳ 208	㉔ 796

Round to the nearest 10.

㉕ 168	㉗ 289	㉙ 103
㉖ 314	㉘ 425	㉚ 97

Round to the nearest 100.

㉛ 756	㉝ 1250	㉟ 3582
㉜ 618	㉞ 2815	㊱ 1539

Copy the sentences. Write the number to the nearest 1000 and use the word `about'.

㊲ The shop sold 1750 decorations in December.

㊳ The plane flew 3963 miles.

㊴ Amber has £5217 in the bank.

㊵ The encyclopaedia has 937 pages.

㊶ The new car cost £18 850.

E Part 1

Copy and complete by choosing one of the numbers in the brackets.

1. 1·9 rounds to (1, 2).

2. 8·1 rounds to (8, 9).

3. 15·2 rounds to (15, 16).

4. 9·8 rounds to (9, 10).

5. 7·1 rounds to (7, 8).

6. 14·2 rounds to (14, 15).

7. 3·9 rounds to (3, 4).

8. 17·7 rounds to (17, 18).

Copy and complete by writing the correct amount in the box. Round to the nearest pound.

9. £12·30 rounds to ☐.

10. £5·80 rounds to ☐.

11. £6·10 rounds to ☐.

12. £3·90 rounds to ☐.

13. £7·20 rounds to ☐.

14. £8·60 rounds to ☐.

15. £4·50 rounds to ☐.

16. £3·40 rounds to ☐.

17. Copy the sentence. Write the number to the nearest 100 and use the word 'about'.
'The cost of the accident was £872.'

Part 2

Round to the nearest whole number.

1. 4·8

2. 6·2

3. 3·5

4. 11·7

5. 8·4

6. 13·3

7. 0·52

8. 5·46

Round to the nearest pound.

9. £8·63

10. £27·27

11. £3·91

12. £6·36

13. £12·80

14. £7·52

15. £4·49

16. £9·78

Round to the nearest metre.

17. 5·6 m

18. 3·9 m

19. 9·7 m

20. 6·3 m

21. 2·8 m

22. 1·49 m

23. 7·5 m

24. 11·9 m

Round to the nearest kilogram.

25. 4·3 kg

26. 3·6 kg

27. 12·2 kg

28. 8·7 kg

29. 5·4 kg

30. 2·5 kg

31. 16·38 kg

32. 7·61 kg

Answer true or false:

33. To the nearest pound, £9·99 rounds to £10.

34. To the nearest metre, 3·45 m rounds to 4 m.

On these pages you will learn about the operations ÷ × + −.

- Consider the possible answers to this question:
  'What is five add seven multiplied by three?'

  By adding first, we obtain: $5 + 7 \times 3$
  $$= 12 \times 3$$
  $$= 36$$

  By multiplying first, we obtain: $5 + 7 \times 3$
  $$= 5 + 21$$
  $$= 26$$

As it stands both answers make perfect sense, though if we could all come up with different answers to the same mathematical question life would be rather stressful as people would have to argue constantly over who is correct.

- The table below shows the order in which everyone must do the given mathematical operations to ensure we all agree.

B rackets	( )	do first	'B'
O			'O'
D ivision	÷	do this pair next	'D'
M ultiplication	×		'M'
A ddition	+	do this pair next	'A'
S ubtraction	−		'S'

Remember the word 'B O D M A S'. (The 'O' is just used to make a word.)

(a) $40 \div 5 + 2$
$$= 8 + 2$$
$$= 10$$

(b) $9 + 8 - 7$
$$= 17 - 7$$
$$= 10$$

(c) $5 + 2 \times 3$ × before +
$$= 5 + 6$$
$$= 11$$

(d) $10 - 8 \div 2$ ÷ before −
$$= 10 - 4$$
$$= 6$$

(e) $4 \times (2 + 3)$
$$= 4 \times 5$$
$$= 20$$

(f) $(6 + 2) \div (5 - 1) + 9$
$$= 8 \div 4 + 9$$
$$= 2 + 9$$
$$= 11$$

M

Work out.

(1) $1 \times 5 + 3$ (9) $6 + 2 \times 4$ (17) $12 \div 3 + 1$ (25) $3 \times 3 + 2 \times 5$

(2) $4 \times 2 - 5$ (10) $3 + 1 \times 6$ (18) $7 + 16 \div 2$ (26) $6 \div 2 + 4 \div 2$

(3) $2 \times 0 + 5$ (11) $8 - 6 \times 1$ (19) $5 + 10 \div 2 + 3$ (27) $4 \div 2 + 2 \times 3$

(4) $2 + 2 \times 4$ (12) $8 + 1 \times 3$ (20) $6 + 2 \times 3 + 2$ (28) $(7 + 2) \div 3$

(5) $3 + 4 \times 2$ (13) $2 + 4 \times 1$ (21) $2 \times 3 + 3 \times 3$ (29) $(6 + 3) \div (5 + 4)$

(6) $3 \times 3 + 1$ (14) $1 + 1 \times 6$ (22) $6 \times 2 + 2 \times 3$ (30) $(16 + 4) \div (5 + 5)$

(7) $4 - 2 \times 2$ (15) $2 \times 3 + 1$ (23) $5 \times 4 + 3 \times 3$

(8) $5 - 1 \times 4$ (16) $6 \div 2 + 1$ (24) $4 \times 1 + 3 \times 2$

(31) **a)** $3 + 1 \times 4$ **b)** $(3 + 1) \times 4$ (34) **a)** $(6 + 3) \div 3$ **b)** $6 + 3 \div 3$

(32) **a)** $3 \times 2 + 5$ **b)** $3 \times (2 + 5)$ (35) **a)** $(1 + 2 + 3) \div 3$ **b)** $1 + 2 + 3 \div 3$

(33) **a)** $4 + 3 \times 2$ **b)** $(4 + 3) \times 2$ (36) **a)** $5 + 1 + 2 \times 3$ **b)** $5 + 1 + (2 \times 3)$

E

Work out.

(1) **a)** $3 + 2 \times 4$ **b)** $(3 + 2) \times 4$

(2) **a)** $3 \times 4 + 5$ **b)** $3 \times (4 + 5)$

(3) **a)** $(5 + 2) \times 3$ **b)** $5 + 2 \times 3$

(4) **a)** $(6 + 6) \div 3$ **b)** $6 + 6 \div 3$

(5) **a)** $(2 + 4 + 6) \div 3$ **b)** $2 + 4 + 6 \div 3$

(6) **a)** $4 + 6 \div 2$ **b)** $(4 + 6) \div 2$

(7) **a)** $(4 + 6) \div (3 + 2)$ **b)** $4 + 6 \div 3 + 2$

(8) **a)** $(5 + 3) \times (2 + 3)$ **b)** $5 + 3 \times 2 + 3$

(9) **a)** $7 + 8 \div 2 + 3$ **b)** $(7 + 8) \div (2 + 3)$

(10) **a)** $5 + 3 \times (2 + 4)$ **b)** $(5 + 3) \times 2 + 4$

(11) **a)** $13 - 2 \times 5$ **b)** $(13 - 2) \times 5$

(12) **a)** $16 \div 4 - 2$ **b)** $16 \div (4 - 2)$

(13) $4 + 8 \times 2 - 18$ (17) $6 + 8 \div 2 + 6$

(14) $3 + 5 \times 2 + 3$ (18) $(2 + 8) \times (3 \times 5) \div (3 + 2)$

(15) $24 \div 6 + 2$ (19) $(3 + 7) \div 2 + 3 \times 4$

(16) $14 \div 2 + 5$ (20) $8 + 4 \div 2 + 3 \times 4$

On these pages you will learn to use metric units of mass and capacity.

- The metric units of mass are kilograms and grams.

    $1000\,g = 1\,kg$

    $500\,g = 0{\cdot}5\,kg$
    $= \text{half a kilogram}$

    $100\,g = 0{\cdot}1\,kg$

    $2500\,g = 2{\cdot}5\,kg$
    $= 2\tfrac{1}{2}\ \text{kilograms}$

Examples

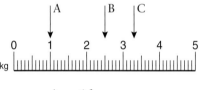

A = 1 kg

B = 2·5 kg

C = 3·3 kg

- Capacity is the amount of liquid that a container can hold.
    The capacity of a bucket is greater than the capacity of a tea cup.

The metric units of capacity are litres and millilitres.

$1000\,ml = 1\ \text{litre}$

$500\,ml = \text{half a litre}$
$= 0{\cdot}5\ \text{litres}$

$100\,ml = 0{\cdot}1\ \text{litres}$

$2500\,ml = 2{\cdot}5\ \text{litres}$

Ⓜ

Copy and complete.

① 4500 g = ☐ kg ☐ g = ☐ kg

② 2500 g = ☐ kg ☐ g = ☐ kg

③ 1500 g = ☐ kg ☐ g = ☐ kg

④ 5000 g = ☐ kg ☐ g = ☐ kg

⑤ 2000 g = ☐ kg ☐ g = ☐ kg

⑥ 6500 g = ☐ kg ☐ g = ☐ kg

⑦ 3500 g = ☐ kg ☐ g = ☐ kg

⑧ 8500 g = ☐ kg ☐ g = ☐ kg

Copy and complete.

⑨ 2500 ml = ☐ ℓ ☐ ml = ☐ ℓ

⑩ 3·5 ℓ = ☐ ℓ ☐ ml = ☐ ℓ

⑪ 8500 ml = ☐ ℓ ☐ ml = ☐ ℓ

⑫ 0·5 ℓ ☐ ml

⑬ 6000 ml ☐ ℓ

⑭ 5·5 ℓ = ☐ ℓ ☐ ml = ☐ ml

Read the measurement shown by the arrow on each dial.

⑮   ⑰   ⑲

⑯   ⑱   ⑳

M

Read the measurement shown by each of the arrows.

(21)

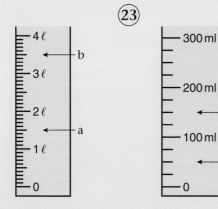

(23)

(22)

(24)

Would you use litres or millilitres to measure the capacity of:

(25) an egg cup

(26) a fish tank

(27) a cereal bowl

(28) a mug

(29) a paddling pool

(30) a wine glass?

E

Write as grams.

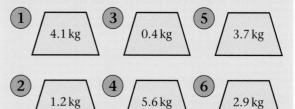

(1) 4.1 kg (3) 0.4 kg (5) 3.7 kg

(2) 1.2 kg (4) 5.6 kg (6) 2.9 kg

Write as kilograms.

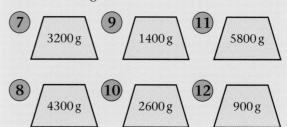

(7) 3200 g (9) 1400 g (11) 5800 g

(8) 4300 g (10) 2600 g (12) 900 g

For each of the scales work out:

a) the measurements shown.

b) the difference between a and b.

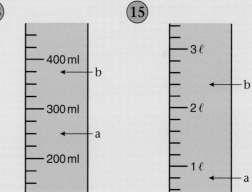

(13)

(15)

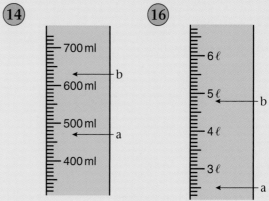

(14)

(16)

On this page you will estimate the metric units for everyday objects.

M

Suggest a suitable metric unit to measure the length of:

(1) a garage

(2) a CD

(3) the M1 motorway

(4) a ladybird

(5) Australia

(6) a biro

(7) a cat

(8) a pea.

Would you expect these things to be longer or shorter than:

| 1 centimetre |

(9) a shirt button

(10) a rubber

(11) an ant

(12) a caterpillar

| 10 centimetres |

(13) a felt tip pen

(14) a finger

(15) a toothbrush

(16) a shoelace

| 1 metre |

(17) a chair leg

(18) the height of a door

(19) the width of a door

(20) a skipping rope.

E

Would you use grams or kilograms to measure the weight of:

(1) an exercise book

(2) a lion

(3) a lawn mower.

(4) a plastic football

(5) a tin of beans

(6) a lorry

Choose the more sensible of the two weights.

(7) a CD   → 70 g   700 g

(8) a man   → 7 kg   70 kg

(9) a counter   → 1g   100g

(10) a car   → 100 kg   1000 kg

(11) a baby   → 300 g   3 kg

(12) an apple   → 100 g   1 kg

Copy each sentence and choose the most sensible estimate.

(13) A paper cup holds (2 ml, 20 ml, 200 ml) of water.

(14) The capacity of a tablespoon is (10 ml, 100 ml, 1000 ml).

(15) A can of cola contains (30 ml, 300 ml, 3000 ml).

(16) A washing up bowl has a capacity of (500 ml, 5 litres, 50 litres).

On this page you will learn to solve problems involving mass.

M

1. A tin of fish weighs 200 g. What do four tins weigh?

2. Keith's father weighs 75 kg. Keith weighs 40 kg less. How much does Keith weigh?

3. A builder loads 43 kg of sand into his van. He adds 26 kg of cement. What is the combined weight of the sand and the cement?

4. A cake weighs one kg. It is cut into five equal slices. How much does each slice weigh?

5. Molly buys 1 kg of carrots. 600 g are eaten. What is the weight of the carrots that are left?

6. A tile weighs 40 g. What is the weight of 10 tiles?

7. A cherry weighs 2 g. Find the weight of a bag of 36 cherries.

E

1. Fifty dictionaries weigh 10 kg. How much does one dictionary weigh?

2. A bag contains 3 kg of flour. 1600 g is used. What is the weight of the flour left in the bag?

3. One tin of peas weighs 300 g. What do 8 tins weigh? Give your answer in kilograms and grams.

4. A small loaf weighs half a kilogram. It is cut into 10 equal slices. What does each slice weigh?

5. A parcel weighs one and a half kilograms. A second parcel weighs 800 g more. What is the combined weight of the parcels?

6. A box of apples weighs 5·2 kg. How much do 100 boxes weigh?

7. Copy and complete the table.

object	mass in g	mass in kg
phone	600 g	
chair		3 kg
parcel	2000 g	

On this page you will learn to solve problems involving capacity.

M

① 3 children share 900 ml of milkshake. How much milkshake does each child have?

② A jar of orange squash is made using 700 ml of water and 200 ml of orange. How much orange squash is there?

③ 6 buckets are used to fill a fish tank. Each bucket holds 4 litres of water. How much water is there in the fish tank?

④ A shop has 58 litres of ice cream. 19 litres is sold. How much ice cream is left?

⑤ There is 150 ml of perfume in one bottle. How much perfume is there in four bottles?

⑥ A shower uses 7 litres of water in one minute. How much water is used in five minutes?

⑦ There is 26 litres of water in a bath. Nine litres came from the cold water tap.
How much water came from the hot water tap?

E

① A carton of cream contains 500 ml. How much cream is needed to fill 10 cartons? Give your answer in litres.

② A container of milk holds 2 litres. 1200 ml is used. How much milk is left?

③ There is 2 litres of orange juice in a jar. It can fill 10 cups. How much orange juice can each cup hold?

④ There is half a litre of cold water in a bowl. 600 ml of hot water is added. How much water is there now in the bowl?

⑤ 8 glasses can be filled from a bottle of lemonade. Each glass holds 250 ml. How much lemonade is in the bottle in litres?

⑥ A full fish tank holds 28 litres of water. The tank is only half full. How much water is in the tank?

⑦ A fast-growing plant 'drinks' 10 ml of water every second.
How many litres of water will the plant drink in 10 minutes?

On this page you will learn to know and use the units of time.

Use these facts:

1 year = 365 days	1 day = 24 hours
= 52 weeks	1 hour = 60 minutes
= 12 months	1 minute = 60 seconds

M

Copy and complete by filling in the box.

1) 1 year = ☐ days
2) 1 year = ☐ weeks
3) 5 weeks = ☐ days
4) 1 year = ☐ months
5) ½ minute = ☐ seconds

6) ☐ years = 36 months
7) ☐ years = 104 weeks
8) ☐ weeks = 28 days
9) ☐ minutes = 180 seconds
10) ☐ minutes = 2 hours

11) How many days are there in June?

12) On which day of the week falls:
   a) June 1st   c) June 6th
   b) June 17th   d) June 28th.

13) How many Sundays are there in the month?

14) How many Thursdays are there?

15) What is the date of the third Monday in the month?

JUNE						
Su	M	Tu	W	Th	F	Sa
				1	2	3	4
5	6	7	8	9	10	11
12	13	14	15	16	17	18
19	29	21	22	23	24	25
26	27	28	29	30		

E

Write as minutes.
1) 10 hours
2) $2\frac{1}{2}$ hours
3) 600 seconds

Write as days.
4) 6 weeks
5) 20 weeks
6) 12 hours

Write as years.
7) 48 months
8) 6 months
9) 520 weeks.

On which day of the week will these children have their birthdays?
10) Marsha   – 14th October
11) Brandon   – 11th October
12) Lauren   – 30th September
13) Samantha – 1st November
14) Ryan   – 18th November

OCTOBER						
Su	M	Tu	W	Th	F	Sa
		1	2	3	4	5
6	7	8	9	10	11	12
13	14	15	16	17	18	19
20	21	22	23	24	25	26
27	28	29	30	31		

On this page you will learn to know and use the units of time.

Analogue clocks have faces.
Read the minutes as:
"past" before 30 minutes.
"to" after 30 minutes.

a.m. means before 12 noon.

Digital clocks have figures only.
The minutes are always shown as
minutes past the hour.

p.m. means after 12 noon.

Examples

quarter to 6   5 minutes past 7   25 minutes to 3
5:45 p.m.   7:05 a.m.   2:35 p.m.

Ⓜ **Part 1**

Write the time shown on each of these clocks in words.

①    ②    ③    ④

⑤    ⑥    ⑦ 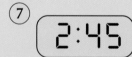   ⑧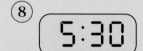

⑨    ⑩    ⑪    ⑫

Part 2

Write the times shown on these clocks:

a) in words

b) in figures, using a.m. and p.m..

| 1 morning | 2 afternoon | 3 morning | 4 afternoon |

| 5 **8:55** evening | 6 **6:10** morning | 7 **10:40** night | 8 **3:20** night |

9) What would be the time if each anologue clock above was 30 minutes fast?

10) What would be the time if each digital clock above was 5 minutes slow?

E

Write the times shown on these clocks:

a) in words

b) in figures, using a.m. and p.m..

| 1 afternoon | 2 morning | 3 night | 4 evening |

| 5 **0:13** lunchtime | 6 **8:42** morning | 7 **1:29** afternoon | 8 **5:54** morning |

9) What would the time be if each of the clocks was 5 minutes slow?

10) What would the time be if each of the clocks was 12 minutes fast?

On these pages you will learn to use timetables.

BBC1		ITV	
2:15	Tennis	3:10	Carry on Nurse (Film)
4:45	Doctor Who (Drama)	4:55	Home and Away (Soap)
5:10	Newsround	5:20	Wheel of Fortune (Game Show)
5:20	Blue Peter	5:50	National News
5:45	Local News	6:28	Weather
6:00	National News	6:30	Local News
6:30	Weather	6:50	Wish You Were Here
6:35	Sports Quiz (Game Show)	7:15	Coronation Street (Soap)
6:55	Gardener's World	7:45	Football
7:30	Eastenders (Soap)	9:40	National News
8:00	Casualty (Drama)	10:00	The Bill (Drama)
8:45	Points of View	11:15	The South Bank Show

Ⓜ **Part 1**

Use the timetable of television programmes.

How long are the following programmes?

(1) Newsround

(2) Blue Peter

(3) Wheel of Fortune

(4) Coronation Street

Which programme could you watch on BBC1 at these times?

(5) 6:00   (6) 8:45   (7) 7:00   (8) 3:30

Which two programmes could you watch at each of these times?

(9) 5:20   (10) 6:30   (11) 4:00   (12) 7:30

(13) The journey from the Station to the Hospital takes
20 minutes.
Buses run every 15 minutes.
Copy and complete the times on this bus timetable.

	Bus 1	Bus 2	Bus 3	Bus 4	Bus 5	Bus 6
Station	9:00	9:15				
Hospital	9:20					

(14) Which bus would a nurse need to be on if she started work at:
     a) 9:30   **b)** 10:30   **c)** 10:15   **d)** 10:45?

Part 2

Use the timetable of television programmes.

How long are the following programmes?

① Doctor Who   ④ Wish You Were Here

② Sports Quiz   ⑤ Tennis

③ The Bill   ⑥ Carry on Nurse

Which two programmes could you watch at each of these times?

⑦ 5:00   ⑧ 5:30   ⑨ 6:40   ⑩ 7:20

⑪ The journey from the Village to the Superstore takes 35 minutes.
Buses run every 20 minutes.
Copy and complete the times on this bus timetable.

	Bus 1	Bus 2	Bus 3	Bus 4	Bus 5	Bus 6
Village	9:15					
Superstore	9:50					

 E

Use the timetable of television programmes.

What is the total length of the following types of programmes?

① Game Shows   ③ Local News   ⑤ Drama

② Soaps   ④ National News   ⑥ Sports

If you watched the following programmes to the end and then changed channels, which programme would you be watching?

⑦ Doctor Who   ⑨ Wish You Were Here   ⑪ Coronation Street

⑧ Sports Quiz   ⑩ Tennis   ⑫ Wheel of Fortune

⑬ Copy and complete this train timetable.
Each train takes the same time between stations.

	Train 1	Train 2	Train 3	Train 4	Train 5	Train 6
Oldport	8:00	8:47	9:23	9:56	10:34	11:09
Highcliff	8:06					
Whitehill	8:19			10:15		
Westham	8:38					
City Centre	8:45		10:08			

On this page you will learn to solve problems involving time.

M

1. Cherie's favourite television programme starts at 6:40. It finishes at 7:20. How long is the programme?

2. Danny left school at 3:20. It took him 25 minutes to walk home. At what time did he arrive home?

3. Lunchtime lasts 50 minutes. It finishes at 1:00. When does it start?

4. A football game starts at 2:10. It lasts 35 minutes. When does it finish?

5. A clock shows the time as 10:20. The real time is 9:55. How many minutes fast is the clock?

6. It takes Carla 25 minutes to walk to the park. She sets off at 2:30. When does she arrive?

7. The food went into the oven at 11:40 and came out at 13:00. For how long was it cooked?

E

1. The pool match lasts 70 minutes. It finishes at 4:30. When does it start?

2. The coach leaves school at 10:38. It arrives at the museum at 11.00. How long is the journey?

3. The P.E. lesson begins at 2:25. It lasts 45 minutes. When does it finish?

4. Mr Carter gets up at 7:10. He leaves for work 40 minutes later. His journey takes 30 minutes. When does he arrive at his office?

5. A film begins at 2:45. It finishes at 4:20. How long is the film?

6. Sita reads for an hour and a half. She starts reading at 6:15. At what time does she finish reading?

7. A train left London at 6:00 pm and arrived in Edinburgh at five minutes to midnight. How long was the journey?

On this page you will learn to solve problems.

M

(1) A newsagent has 100 newspapers.
He sells 68.
How many newspapers are left?

(2) Neil saves £4 every week. How long will it take him to save £28?

(3) There are 70 apples on a tree.
25 apples are picked.
8 more fall off the tree.
How many apples are left on the tree?

(4) It takes Stacey four minutes to read one page. There are 20 pages in her book.
How long will it take her to read the book?

(5) Jamie buys three packets of 8 Christmas cards and one box of 25 cards.
How many cards has he bought?

(6) Helen is 33 years old. Sally is 21 years older.
How old is Sally?

(7) Darren has 23 jigsaw pieces.
Nathan has 12 more than Darren.
How many pieces do they have altogether?

(8) There are 48 biscuits in a tin. Half of them are eaten.
13 more are eaten.
How many biscuits are left?

E

(1) How many days are there in six weeks?

(2) There are 94 people on a tall ship. 59 get off.
How many people are left on the tall ship?

(3) Sarah's book has 68 pages. She needs to read 5 more pages to reach half way. What page is she on?

(4) Eight children shared 40 sweets equally between them.
How many sweets did each child receive?

(5) Jason has 17 more books on his top shelf than on his bottom shelf.
He has 45 books on his top shelf.
How many books does Jason have altogether?

(6) There are 65 adults and 47 children on a train.
How many people are there on the train?

(7) Four classes in a school have 25 children each.
The other four classes have 30 children each.
How many children are there in the school?

(8) There are 84 cars parked in a car park. 67 more cars are parked.
54 cars drive out. How many cars are left in the car park?

On these pages you will learn to solve money problems and to change pounds to pence and pence to pounds.

Examples

170p = £1·70   205p = £2·05

SCHOOL SHOP PRICES			
pencil	15p	T-shirt	£3·20
pen	45p	sweatshirt	£8·80
ruler	25p	dictionary	£3·75
rubber	20p	calculator	£2·50
felt tips (pack)	80p	geometry set	£4·25
crayons (pack)	75p	homework bag	£3·50
sharpener	30p	P.E. bag	£2·30

Ⓜ

Change to pence.

(1) £2·30

(2) £3·85

(3) £6·42

(4) £8·15

Change to pounds and pence.

(5) 235p

(6) 460p

(7) 523p

(8) 745p

Work out the cost of these items and the change from £5·00.

(9) 1 T-shirt, 4 rulers

(10) 1 calculator, 1 P.E. bag

(11) 1 geometry set, 1 pen

(12) 1 dictionary, 2 rubbers

(13) 4 packs of crayons

(14) 2 pens, 4 pencils

(15) 1 calculator, 2 pens

(16) 3 packs of felt tips

How many of these items can you buy for £5·00?

(17) rulers

(18) P.E. bags

(19) rubbers

(20) crayons

Copy and complete by writing the missing number in the box.

(21) £10 = ☐ × 50p

(22) £10 = ☐ × 20p

(23) £10 = ☐ × 10p

(24) £10 = ☐ × 5p

(25) £5 = ☐ × 50p

(26) £5 = ☐ × 20p

(27) £5 = ☐ × 5p

(28) £5 = ☐ × 1p

(29) £20 = ☐ × 50p

(30) £20 = ☐ × 20p

(31) £20 = ☐ × 10p

(32) £20 = ☐ × 5p

E

Change to pence.

① £7·26   ③ £3·72

② £4·04   ④ £9·08

Change to pounds and pence.

⑤ 257p   ⑦ 516p

⑥ 349p   ⑧ 74p

Work out the cost of these items and the change from £10·00.

⑨ 3 T-shirts

⑩ 1 calculator, 2 pens

⑪ 6 rubbers, 1 homework bag

⑫ 1 sweatshirt, 3 rulers

⑬ 30 pencils

⑭ 1 P.E. bag, 4 sharpeners

⑮ 8 packs of crayons

⑯ 2 geometry sets, 1 pen

How many of these items could you buy for £10·00?

⑰ felt tips

⑱ calculators

⑲ pens

⑳ homework bags.

㉑ You buy a geometry set, two packs of felt tips and one other item. You pay with a £10 note and receive £3·95 change. What is the other item?

㉒ You buy a dictionary, a sweatshirt and one other item. You pay with a £20·00 note and receive £5·15 change. What is the other item?

㉓ The manager of the school shop has £200 to spend. A pack of crayons costs £15. How many of the packs can the manager buy?

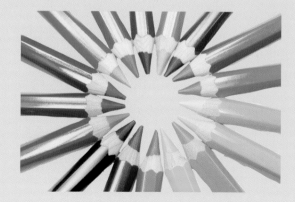

On these pages you will learn to draw and interpret graphs and charts.

Line graphs are graphs in which a set of data is plotted and the points are joined up with a line. Line graphs often show a trend.

Example

This line graph shows the average daily maximum temperature in London during the year.

Month	J F M A M J J A S O N D
Temperature (°C)	4 5 7 9 12 16 18 17 15 11 8 5

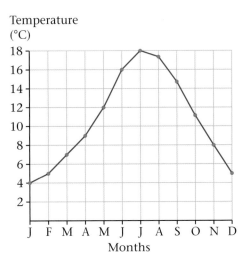

M

Match each of these statements to one of the graphs.

1. The temperature rises steadily.

2. The temperature begins to rise and then falls quickly.

3. The temperature rises more and more quickly.

4. The temperature stays the same and then falls quickly.

5. The temperature falls faster and faster.

6. The temperature rises, stays the same and then rises quickly.

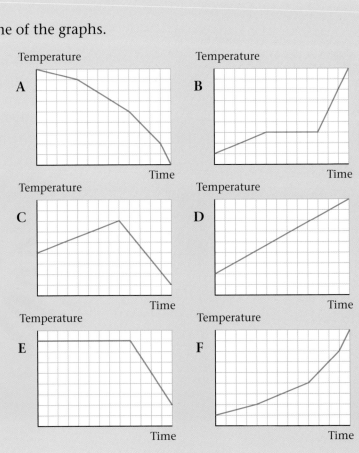

(7) The children in 7Z were asked how many children were there in their family. These are the results:

Make a tally chart and then draw a bar chart to show the results.

Results

2	3	1	2	4	3	1	2
3	4	2	3	1	5	3	2
2	1	2	5	3	2	2	3
2	3	4	1	2	3	2	1

(8) This bar chart shows the number of vowels in the first page of a book.
   a) Which was the most common vowel?
   b) Which was the least common vowel?
   c) How many As were there?
   d) How many Us were there?
   e) Which letter appeared half as often as E?

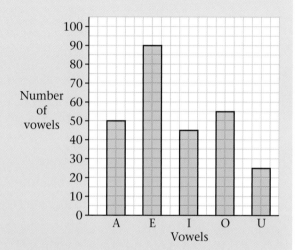

(9) This line graph shows the depth of water in a stream throughout the year.
   a) How deep was the stream in March?
   b) In which two months was the stream 8 cm deep?
   c) Which month saw the largest increase in depth? Why do you think this happened?
   d) What was the range of the depths?

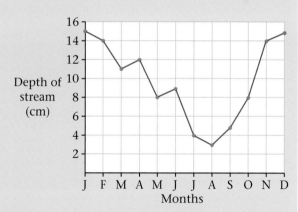

(10) The table shows the results of Sara's weekly tables test.
Use the data to draw a line graph. Remember to label the axes.

Week	1	2	3	4	5	6	7	8	9	10
Mark	3	4	5	6	5	6	6	7	8	9

E

(1) John wanted to know how long the
words were in his reading book.
He found that in one passage the
words had these numbers of letters:

Make a tally chart and then draw a bar
chart to show the results.

Results

3	3	4	4	4	3	7	4	2	2
2	7	2	6	2	8	2	2	4	5
2	7	5	2	3	4	6	3	5	2
3	5	7	2	2	7	4	3	5	6
5	3	2	8	2	4	6	7	3	4

(2) This bar chart shows the number of
diners at a restaurant.
   a) How many diners were there
       on Thursday?
   b) How many more diners were
       there on Friday than on Monday?
   c) Which day had the most diners?
       Explain why.
   d) Which day had the least diners?
   e) How many people dined at the
       restaurant during the week?

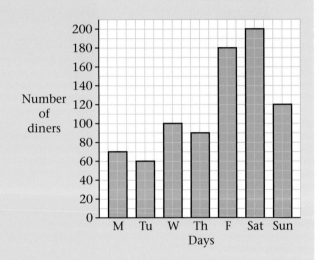

(3) This line graph shows the average daily
temperature in Sweden.
   a) What was the temperature in June?
   b) In which month was the
       temperature 7°C?
   c) In which two months was the
       temperature 3°C?
   d) Which two months saw the largest
       fall in temperature?
   e) What was the range of temperature
       over the year?

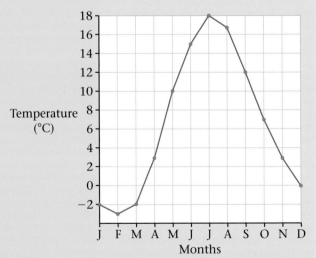

On this page you will learn to use near doubles to add or subtract.

> **Examples**
> 35 + 37 = 35 + 35 + 2 = Double 35 + 2 = 70 + 2 = 72
> 18 + 16 = 18 + 18 − 2 = Double 18 − 2 = 36 − 2 = 34

M

Work out:

1. 25 + 26
2. 16 + 18
3. 70 + 80
4. 55 + 53
5. 90 + 80
6. 35 + 34
7. 60 + 70
8. 18 + 20
9. 16 + 14
10. 80 + 70
11. 65 + 66
12. 19 + 17
13. 80 + 90
14. 85 + 87
15. 17 + 18
16. 75 + 74.

E

Work out:

1. 460 + 460
2. 290 + 290
3. 370 + 370
4. 480 + 480
5. 390 + 390
6. 280 + 280
7. 360 + 360
8. 470 + 470.

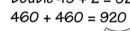

> 46 + 46 =
> Double 45 + 2 = 92
> 460 + 460 = 920

● Now you will practise doubling and halving and learn to use partitioning to double and halve.

Examples
Double 34 = (30 × 2) + (4 × 2) = 60 + 8 = 68
Half of 76 = (70 ÷ 2) + (6 ÷ 2) = 35 + 3 = 38

M

Write the answer only.

1. 16 × 2
2. 21 × 2
3. 34 × 2
4. 27 × 2
5. 230 × 2

6. 380 × 2
7. 490 × 2
8. 440 × 2
9. 2200 × 2
10. 3900 × 2

11. 42 ÷ 2
12. 64 ÷ 2
13. 88 ÷ 2
14. 54 ÷ 2
15. 760 ÷ 2

16. 940 ÷ 2
17. 680 ÷ 2
18. 5600 ÷ 2
19. 3600 ÷ 2
20. 7400 ÷ 2

E

Work out by partitioning.

1. 64 × 2
2. 56 × 2
3. 78 × 2
4. 93 × 2
5. 67 × 2

6. 162 ÷ 2
7. 134 ÷ 2
8. 158 ÷ 2
9. 178 ÷ 2
10. 116 ÷ 2

These pages will help you to collect some data, draw a chart and say something about what you have found (interpret the data).

Task

How many bars of chocolate did children in my class eat last week?
(Your teacher should help you).

Copy and complete this tally chart by asking all the people in your class. (If a person says more than 10 bars, put them in the 10 bars part).

Use |||| in your tally if you have 4 people.
Use |||| tally in your tally if you have 5 people.

Now add up your tally numbers. We call this the frequency (how many).

Copy and complete this frequency table.

Number of bars of chocolate	Tally
0	
1	
2	
3	
4	
5	
6	
7	
8	
9	
10	

Number of bars of chocolate	Frequency
0	
1	
2	
3	
4	
5	
6	
7	
8	
9	
10	

You must now show this data on a bar chart.

On squared paper, copy this, (you only have to go up to your highest frequency number).

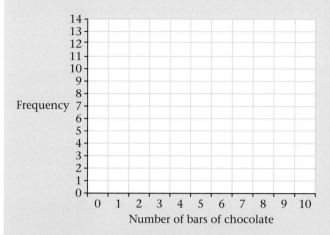

Look at your frequency table and draw bars. Here is an example.

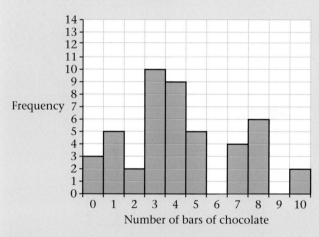

The tallest bar tells you which 'number of chocolate bars' had the most number of people.

This is the mode (the most frequent).

In the example, '3 bars of chocolate' had the most people (the mode is 3 bars of chocolate).

Write down the mode from your bar chart (there might be more than one mode).

Did you expect this to be the mode?

If you had time, what else could you find out about chocolate? Maybe how much money children in your class spent on chocolate in the last week?

E

This needs a computer with a spreadsheet. Teachers note: See answer book for help with using 'Excel'.

Task 1

Do the chocolate survey on a spreadsheet. You need to make and print a title, a frequency table and a bar chart with labels.

(You may need to do some spreadsheet work with your teacher first).

Finally, write on the mode (or type it) and anything else you want to say.

Task 2

Can you use the spreadsheet to make and print out a pie chart instead of a bar chart?

Task 3

If you have time, find out how much money children in your class spent on chocolate in the last week.

Can you make and print a title, a frequency table and a bar chart with labels for this data?

Can you find a mode for the amount of money spent on chocolate?

On these pages you will look again at recognising triangular and square numbers.

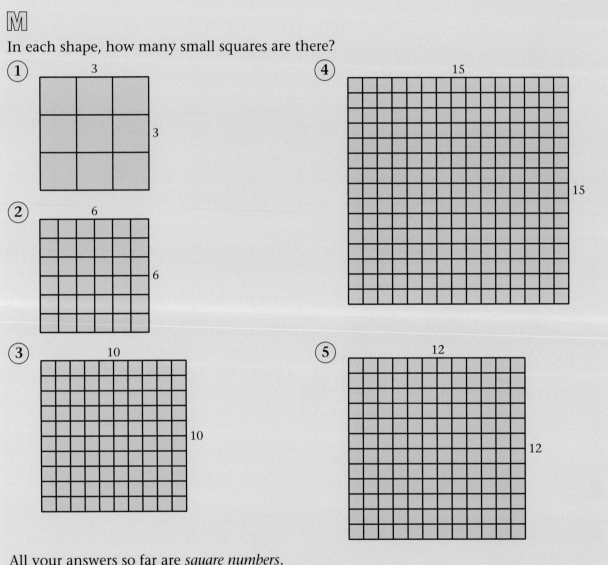

M

In each shape, how many small squares are there?

① 3 × 3

② 6 × 6

③ 10 × 10

④ 15 × 15

⑤ 12 × 12

All your answers so far are *square numbers*.

⑥ If a big square is cut up into 16 equal small squares, how long is one side of the big square?

⑦ If a big square is cut up into 49 equal small squares, how long is one side of the big square?

⑧ If a big square is cut up into 81 equal small squares, how long is one side of the big square?

⑨ If a big square is cut up into 144 equal small squares, how long is one side of the big square?

10 a) Copy and draw the next 3 shapes in this pattern.

b) Write down the number of black triangles for each shape in your pattern.

These should be the first 7 *TRIANGULAR NUMBERS*.

11 Write down the next 3 numbers in this pattern:

$$15, \quad 21, \quad 28, \quad 36, \quad ?, \quad ?, \quad ?$$

12 Copy this triangle of numbers (called Pascal's triangle).

```
                1
              1   1
            1   2   1
          1   3   3   1
        1   4   6   4   1
      1   5  10  10   5   1
    1   6  15  20  15   6   1
  1   7  21  35  35  21   7   1
```

Look for the first 6 triangular numbers and put a circle around each one.

REMEMBER: Triangular Numbers are

$$1 \qquad 3 \qquad 6 \qquad 10$$

E

Work out

1 5^2 **4** 8^2 **7** $4^2 + 3^2$ **10** $10^2 - 8^2$

2 6^2 **5** 11^2 **8** $5^2 + 6^2$ **11** $8^2 - 6^2$

3 7^2 **6** 13^2 **9** $9^2 - 7^2$ **12** $7^2 + 9^2$

13 Suppose you add the first two triangular numbers.
You get $1 + 3 = 4$ and 4 is a square number.
a) Add the second and third triangular numbers.
b) Add the third and fourth triangular numbers.
c) Add the fourth and fifth triangular numbers.
d) Do you always get a square number when you add two consecutive triangular numbers?

On this page you will learn to extend number sequences and to find rules.

To find the rule that links the numbers study the gaps.

Examples

1 3 5 7 9	The rule is 'add 2'.
20 17 14 11 8	The rule is 'subtract 3'.
−3 −2 −1 0 1	The rule is 'add 1'.

M

Copy the sequences and write the next three numbers. What is the rule for each sequence?

1. 57 59 61 63
2. 126 122 118 114
3. 46 53 60 67
4. 65 56 47 38

5. 30 70 110 150
6. 137 134 131 128
7. 35 60 85 110
8. 28 36 44 52

9. 78 73 68 63
10. 12 27 42 57
11. 475 450 425 400
12. 57 63 69 75

13. 105 90 75 60
14. 93 86 79 72
15. 7 15 23 31
16. 243 354 465 576

17. 19 22 25 28
18. 141 130 119 108
19. 90 150 210 270
20. 45 90 135 180

E

Copy and complete by filling in the boxes.

1. −5 −4 ☐ ☐ ☐ 0 1
2. 3 2 ☐ ☐ ☐ −2 −3
3. ☐ ☐ ☐ −6 −4 −2 0
4. −14 −10 ☐ −2 ☐ 6 ☐
5. −7 −5 ☐ −1 ☐ 3 ☐
6. 5 3 1 −1 ☐ ☐ ☐
7. −6 −4 ☐ ☐ ☐ 4 6
8. −6 −7 ☐ ☐ ☐ −11 −12

Copy and complete each number sequence.

9. −11 −9 −7 −5 ☐ ☐ ☐
10. −11 −8 −5 ☐ ☐ ☐ 7
11. −6 −4 ☐ ☐ ☐ 4 6
12. −14 −10 ☐ ☐ ☐ 6 10
13. 5 3 1 ☐ ☐ ☐ −7
14. 8 6 4 2 ☐ ☐ ☐
15. 11 8 5 2 ☐ ☐ ☐
16. 13 9 5 ☐ ☐ ☐ −11

On this page you will work with square numbers and square roots.

> When a number is multiplied by itself you get a square number.
> They are called square numbers because they make square patterns.
>
> The square root of a number is the number which is multiplied by
> itself to give that number. The symbol for square root is $\sqrt{\ }$.
> So $\sqrt{9} = 3$, $\sqrt{16} = 4$, $\sqrt{100} = 10$
>
>
>
> $3^2 = 3 \times 3 = 9$

M

(1) Copy and complete.

$6^2 = 6 \times 6 = \boxed{}$

Work out

(2) $4^2 + 2^2$ (8) $10^2 + 7^2$

(3) $5^2 + 3^2$ (9) $9^2 + 1^2$

(4) $6^2 + 1^2$ (10) $8^2 + 5^2$

(5) $5^2 - 3^2$ (11) $9^2 - 4^2$

(6) $8^2 - 6^2$ (12) $10^2 - 6^2$

(7) $6^2 - 3^2$ (13) $8^2 - 7^2$

Work out the following. You can use a calculator.

(14) $\sqrt{36}$ (20) $\sqrt{144} - \sqrt{100}$

(15) $\sqrt{196}$ (21) $\sqrt{9} + \sqrt{49}$

(16) $\sqrt{625}$ (22) $\sqrt{64} + \sqrt{1}$

(17) $\sqrt{64} + \sqrt{25}$ (23) $\sqrt{196} - \sqrt{169}$

(18) $\sqrt{81} - \sqrt{25}$ (24) $\sqrt{400} - \sqrt{100}$

(19) $\sqrt{100} - \sqrt{49}$ (25) $\sqrt{121} + \sqrt{144}$

(26) Answer true or false
'The number of squares
on a chessboard is
a square number.'

E

Use a calculator to work out

(1) 20^2 (5) 31^2

(2) 21^2 (6) 13^2

(3) 19^2 (7) 40^2

(4) 15^2 (8) 100^2

Use a calculator to find out which number, when multiplied by itself, gives a product of:

(9) 729   (13) 2116

(10) 196   (14) 784

(11) 1225   (15) 1024

(12) 484   (16) 6889.

Here are the first ten square numbers:
1   4   9   16   25   36   49   64   81   100

Find a pair of square numbers which give a total of:

(17) 13   (21) 73

(18) 40   (22) 181

(19) 125   (23) 97

(20) 74   (24) 113.

Find a pair of square numbers which give a difference of:

(25) 7   (29) 80

(26) 84   (30) 300

(27) 45   (31) 32

(28) 39   (32) 105.

On these pages you will learn to use co-ordinates to find the position of a point on a grid.

Ⓜ

① Draw a 10 × 10 grid.

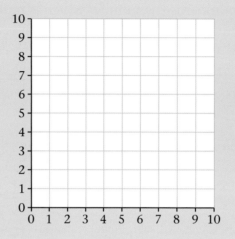

Plot the points in the first column.
Join them up in the order given.
You should have drawn a letter.

Do the same for the other columns
using the same grid.

(4, 6)	(2, 5)	(7, 1)	(10, 7)
(4, 10)	(2, 6)	(7, 4)	(9, 8)
(6, 10)	(0, 6)	(5, 4)	(8, 7)
(6, 8)	(0, 2)	(5, 0)	(10, 5)
(4, 8)	(2, 2)	(7, 0)	(9, 4)
(6, 6)	(2, 3)	(7, 1)	(8, 5)
	(3, 3)	(8, 0)	

② Use the grid below to work out the message written in co-ordinates.
Work *down* each column.

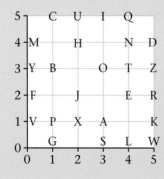

(5, 0)	(0, 3)	(1, 3)	(2, 1)	(1, 5)
(2, 4)		(4, 2)		(5, 2)
(0, 3)	(1, 0)	(1, 5)	(3, 5)	(3, 3)
	(3, 3)	(3, 1)	(3, 0)	(3, 0)
(5, 4)		(2, 5)		(3, 0)
(3, 3)	(2, 5)	(3, 0)	(3, 1)	
(4, 2)	(1, 1)	(4, 2)		
(3, 0)	?			

③ Draw a grid on squared paper like this.
Label across from 0 to 18 (horizontal axis).
Label up from 0 to 28 (vertical axis).
Plot the points below and join them up with
a ruler in the order given.

(10, 28) (16, 28) (18, 26) (18, 24) (16, 22)
$(14\frac{1}{2}, 20)$ (14, 18) (14, 8) (12, 6) (12, 1)

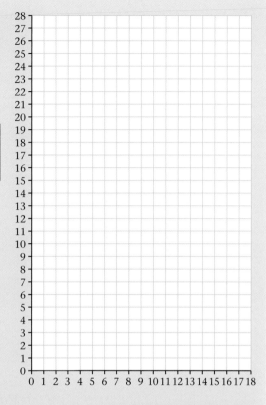

ON THE SAME PICTURE plot the points below and join them up with a ruler in the order given.

DO NOT JOIN THE LAST POINT IN THE BOX ABOVE WITH THE FIRST POINT IN THE NEW BOX.

(5, 1)   (7, 3)   (7, 5)   (6, 6)   (5, 6)   (4, 7)   (6, 7)   (8, 7)   (10, 8)

ON THE SAME PICTURE plot the points below and join them up with a ruler in the order given.

(4, 7)   (3, 8)   (4, 9)   (6, 9)

ON THE SAME PICTURE plot the points below and join them up with a ruler in the order given.

(4, 9)   (4, 10)   (5, 10)

ON THE SAME PICTURE plot the points below and join them up with a ruler in the order given.

(7, 12)   (6, 13)   (5, 13)   (4, 12)   (4, 11)   (5, 10)   (6, 10)
(7, 11)   (7, 12)   (8, 13)   (9, 13)   (10, 12)   (10, 11)   (9, 10)
(8, 10)   (7, 11)

ON THE SAME PICTURE plot the points below and join them up with a ruler in the order given.

(10, 28)	(8, 26)	(7, 24)	$(6\frac{1}{2}, 22)$	(6, 20)	$(5\frac{1}{2}, 18)$
(5, 16)	(5, 13)	$(5, 13\frac{1}{2})$	(7, 14)	(9, 14)	(12, 13)	(12, 6)

Draw a ⊕ around the points below, making ⊕⊕⊕⊕⊕

the circles touch like this

(7, 4)　(8, 4)　(9, 4)　(10, 4)　(11, 4)　(12, 4)

Draw a • at (6, 11) and a • at (9, 11)

Who am I?　　　Colour me in?

E

1 Use the grid below to work out the joke written in co-ordinates.
Work *across* each row.

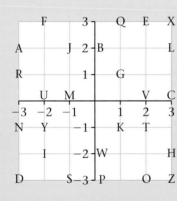

(0, −2) (3, −2) (−3, 2) (2, −1)　(−3, −3) (2, −3)
(−2, −1) (2, −3) (−2, 0)
(3, 0) (−3, 2) (3, 2) (3, 2)　(−3, 2)　(2, −3) (−3, −1) (2, 3)
(2, 3) (−2, −1) (2, 3) (−3, −3)
(−3, −3) (−2, −2) (−3, −1) (2, −3)
　(−1, −3) (−3, 2) (−2, 0) (−3, 1)?
(−3, −3) (2, −3) (−2, −1) (2, −3) (−2, 0) (2, −1) (3, −2)
　(−2, −2) (−3, −1) (1, −1) (2, −1) (3, −2)
(2, 3) (−2, −1) (−1, −3) (−3, 2)
　(−2, 0) (−3, 1) (−2, 0) (−1, −3).

2 Draw a grid like the one above.

Plot the points for Shape A and join them up in the given order.

Use a different colour for each shape. Can you name each of the shapes?

A	B	C	D
(−3, −2)	(−1, −1)	(3, −1)	(−1, 1)
(−1, 2)	(−2, 1)	(−3, 1)	(1, −1)
(3, 0)	(2, 3)	(−1, 3)	(−1, −3)
	(3, 1)		(−3, −1)

1 Write down the number in each empty box.

a) $6 \times \boxed{} = 42$

b) $36 \div \boxed{} = 4$

c) $(4 \times 8) - \boxed{} = 22$

2 Find these numbers, write down the number nearest to 1000.

(1099)   (970)   (879)   (949)   (1045)

3 Write down all the multiples of 8 in this list of numbers.

(14)   (44)   (32)   (48)   (58)

4 Work out $568 \div 8$

5 Rob has £70.
CDs cost £9 each.
How many CDs can he buy?

6 37 children each have 4 computer games.
How many computer games do they have in total?

7

Is the time shown on this clock

   9:40   10:40   7:50   8:10   or   10:08 ?

130

8) These are the opening times of a supermarket.

	opening times		
	a.m.		p.m.
Monday	8:00	to	8:00
Tuesday	8:00	to	8:00
Wednesday	8:00	to	9:00
Thursday	8:00	to	10:00
Friday	7:00	to	10:00
Saturday	7:00	to	8:00
Sunday	10:00	to	4:00

a) How many hours is the supermarket open on Sunday?

b) Asif arrives at the supermarket at 9:10 p.m. on Friday.
How many minutes is it before the supermarket closes?

9) Work out

a) 23×43

b) 235×39

10) There are 16 cans of coke in a box.
A shop buys 18 boxes.
How many cans does the shop buy in total?

11) Write down which of these numbers is divisible by 4.

 34   112   105   220   324

12) Work out

a) $8 + 3 \times 4$

b) $(6 + 2) \times 4 - 4$

13) Put these numbers in order with the smallest first:

 5617   5647   5592   5702

(14) William has two cans of drink.
Each can contains 175ml.

He empties them both into a beaker.

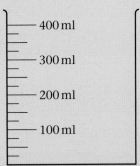

Copy this part of the scale:

Draw an arrow (→) to show the level of the liquid in the beaker.

(15) 3 pieces of metal weigh:

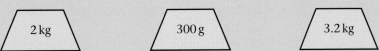

The 3 pieces of metal are melted down and made into one metal ball.
How much does the metal ball weigh?

(16) Find all the pairs of factors of the number 20.

(17) Which number is the larger?

$$\sqrt{36} \quad \text{or} \quad 3^2$$

(18) This line graph shows the average daily temperature in Bristol one year.

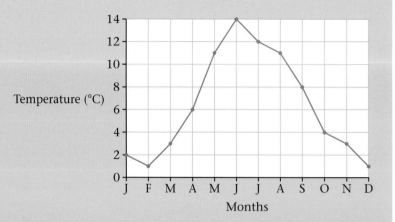

a) What was the temperature in April?

b) In which month was the temperature 8°C?

c) Between which two months was the rise in temperature largest?

(19) Cherie buys a magazine for £1·60, a drink for 65p and some crisps for 40p.

a) How much does she spend?

b) How much change from £10 would she get?

(20)

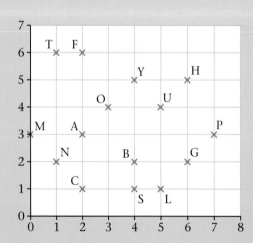

Write down the letter at each of the following co-ordinates to make a word.

(6,5)   (2,3)   (5,1)   (1,6)

On this page you will try to complete the crossnumber puzzles.

Copy the crossnumber puzzles onto 1 cm squared paper.
Use the clues to solve the puzzles.

A

Clues across	Clues down
1) 34 + 35	1) 44 + 19
3) 36 − 9	2) 1000 − 49
5) 75 − 40	3) 23 × 10
6) 6 × 5	4) 700 ÷ 10
7) 85 + 85	8) 96 − 21
11) 32 − 15	9) 54 + 7
12) 19 × 2	10) 36 ÷ 2

B

Clues across	Clues down
1) 28 ÷ 2	1) 96 + 30
3) 49 + 19	2) 12 × 4
5) 7 × 4	3) 665 − 50
6) 100 − 81	4) 101 − 12
7) 8·5 × 10	7) 45 + 36
8) 7 × 3	8) 50 ÷ 2
10) 30 ÷ 2	9) 6 × 4
11) 47 + 47	

C

Clues across	Clues down
1) 436 + 57	1) 8 × 6
4) 29 × 3	2) 132 − 35
5) 360 ÷ 4	3) 0·6 × 100
6) 9 × 8	5) 37 × 25
7) 113 − 44	7) 9 × 7
9) 6 × 9	8) 460 ÷ 5
11) 40 × 8	10) 7^2

Reflective Symmetry 1

On these pages you will learn to recognise line symmetry in 2-D shapes.

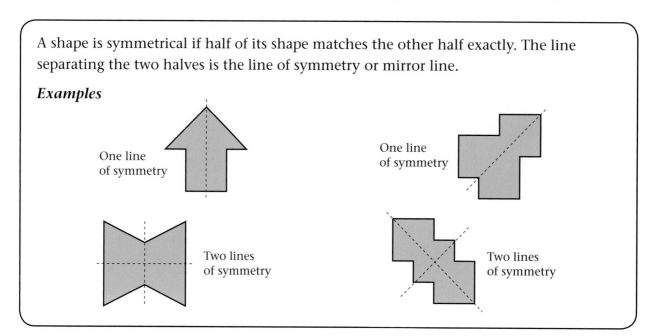

A shape is symmetrical if half of its shape matches the other half exactly. The line separating the two halves is the line of symmetry or mirror line.

Examples

One line of symmetry

One line of symmetry

Two lines of symmetry

Two lines of symmetry

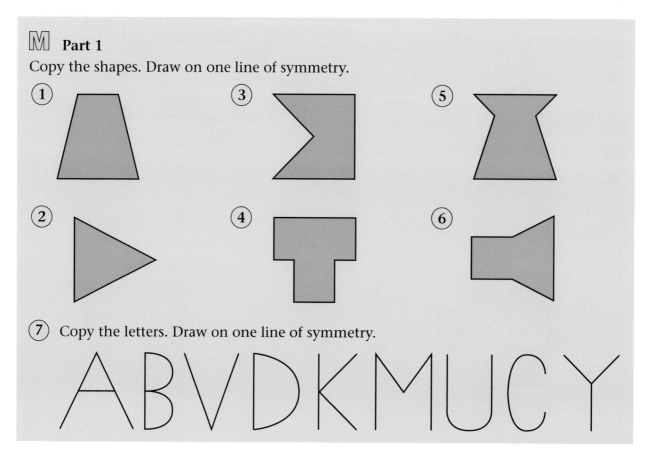

Ⓜ **Part 1**

Copy the shapes. Draw on one line of symmetry.

① ③ ⑤

② ④ ⑥

⑦ Copy the letters. Draw on one line of symmetry.

ABVDKMUCY

Part 1
Copy the shapes onto squared paper.
Draw two lines of symmetry on each shape.

E

Copy the patterns below onto squared paper. Shade in as many squares as necessary to complete the symmetrical patterns.

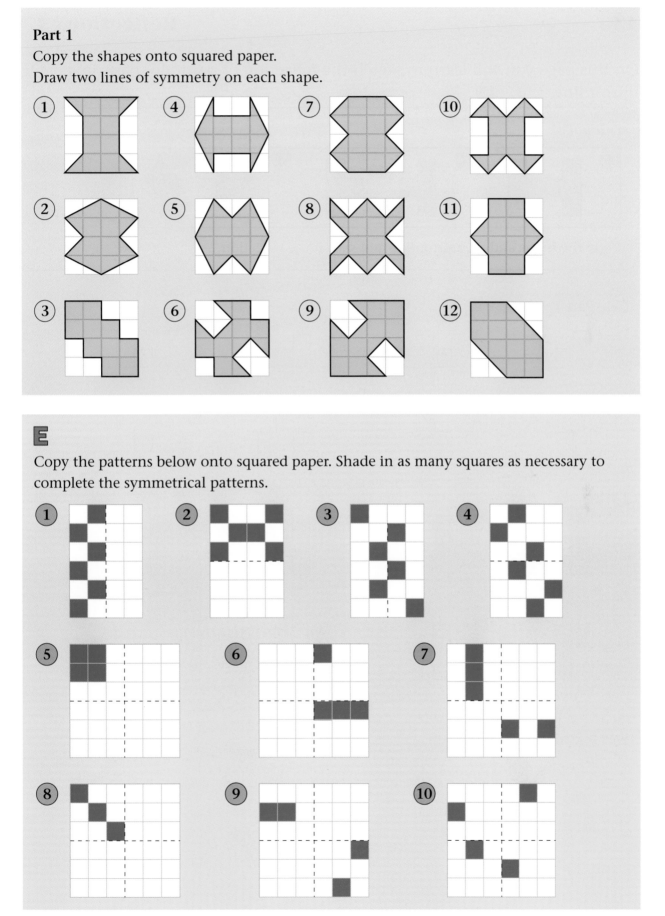

On this page you will learn to sketch the reflection of a simple shape in a mirror line.

Examples

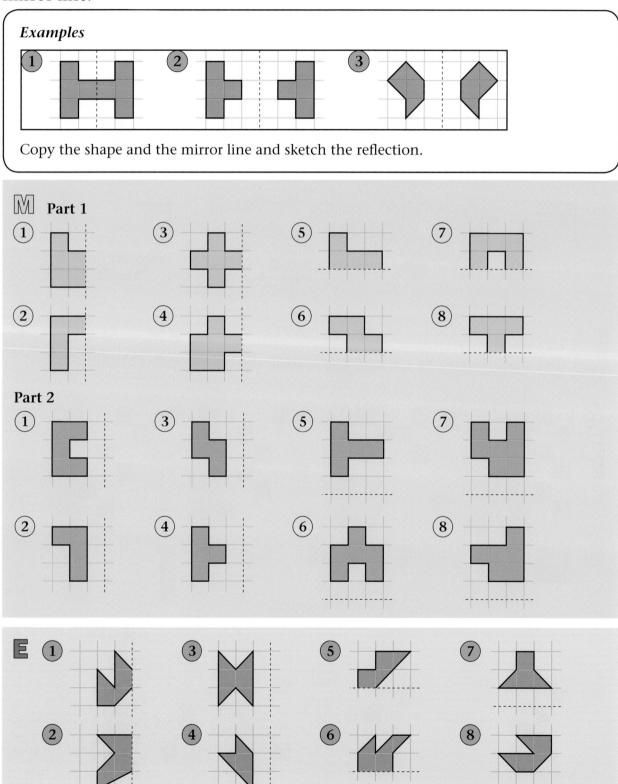

Copy the shape and the mirror line and sketch the reflection.

On this page you will learn to make patterns by repeatedly translating a shape.

Translating a shape means moving it in a straight line.

Example

Make a pattern by repeatedly translating a shape:

a) one square horizontally.   **b)** one square vertically.   **c)** half a square horizontally.

Ⓜ

① Use any of the shapes below or make up your own shapes.
Make a pattern by repeatedly translating shapes one square:
  a) in a horizontal line.   **b)** in a vertical line.

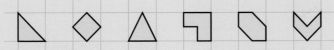

② Use any of the shapes above, or make up your own shape.
Repeatedly translate the shape in a horizontal line:
  a) $\frac{1}{2}$ square   **b)** 2 squares   **c)** $1\frac{1}{2}$ squares.

③ Use the same shape. Do exactly the same but this time work vertically.

Ⓔ

① The isosceles triangle is made in two squares.
Here it is repeatedly translated two squares.
Use the same shape but repeatedly translate it:
  a) 1 square   **b)** $\frac{1}{2}$ square   **c)** $1\frac{1}{2}$ squares.

② Investigate the patterns made by repeatedly translating other shapes made in two squares.

On these pages you will learn to estimate, measure and draw angles accurately.

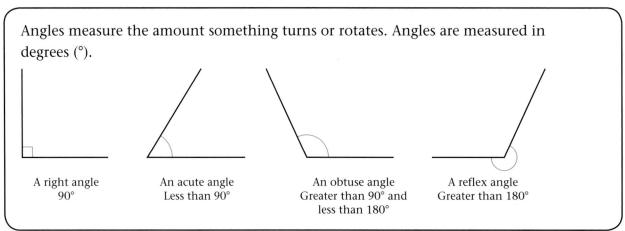

Angles measure the amount something turns or rotates. Angles are measured in degrees (°).

A right angle   An acute angle   An obtuse angle   A reflex angle
90°   Less than 90°   Greater than 90° and   Greater than 180°
                                               less than 180°

Ⓜ

Decide which is the correct angle from the two answers.
Do not measure the angles.

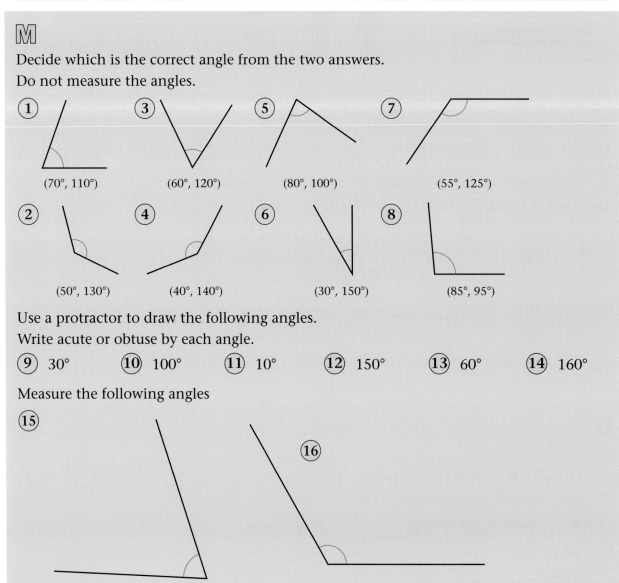

① (70°, 110°)   ③ (60°, 120°)   ⑤ (80°, 100°)   ⑦ (55°, 125°)

② (50°, 130°)   ④ (40°, 140°)   ⑥ (30°, 150°)   ⑧ (85°, 95°)

Use a protractor to draw the following angles.
Write acute or obtuse by each angle.

⑨ 30°   ⑩ 100°   ⑪ 10°   ⑫ 150°   ⑬ 60°   ⑭ 160°

Measure the following angles

⑮

⑯

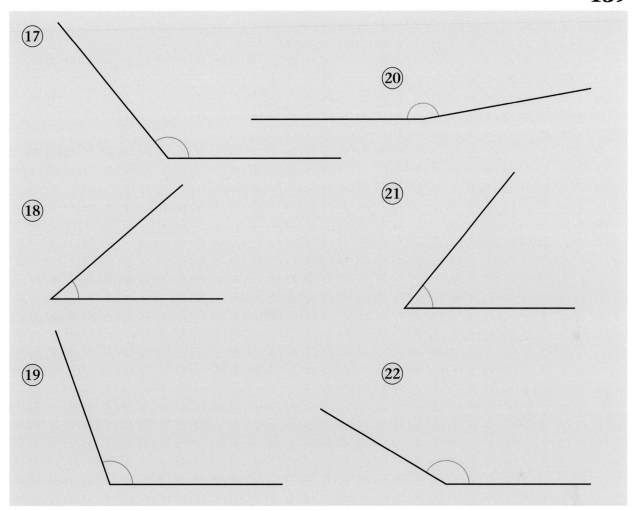

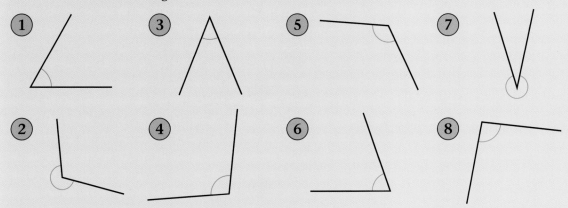

E

State whether the following angles are acute, obtuse or reflex.
Do not measure the angles

Use a protractor to draw the following angles.
Write acute or obtuse by each angle.

 45°   145°   25°   125°   75°   155°

Measure the following angles.

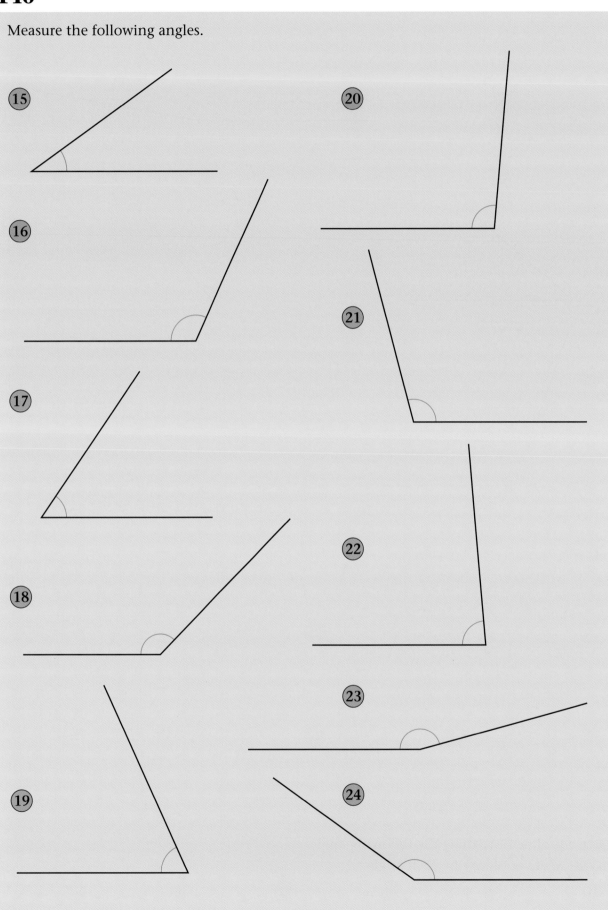

15

16

17

18

19

20

21

22

23

24

On this page you will learn to calculate angles on a straight line.

Example

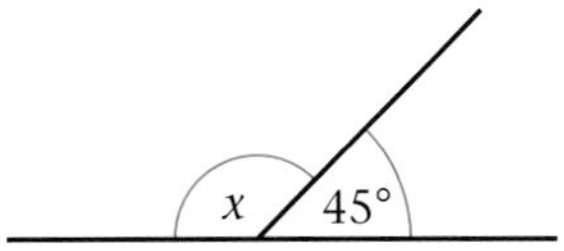

$x + 45° = 180°$

$x = 135°$

Ⓜ

Calculate the missing angles.

① 150° a

⑤ c 80°

⑨ 65° e

⑬ g 55°

② 110° b

⑥ d 60°

⑩ 125° f

⑭ h 95°

③ 75° i

⑦ k 48°

⑪ 59° m

⑮ o 37°

④ 136° j

⑧ l 142°

⑫ 154° n

⑯ p 113°

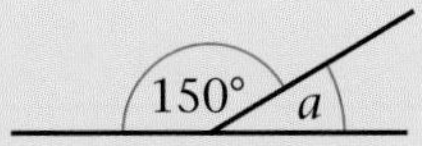

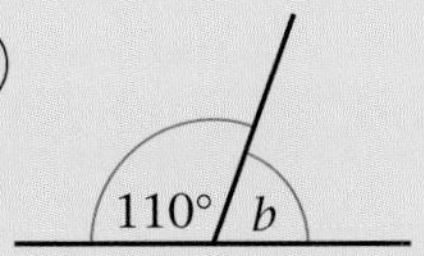

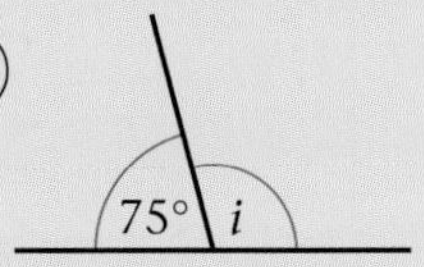

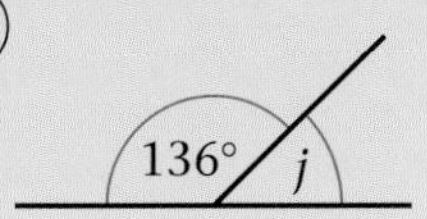

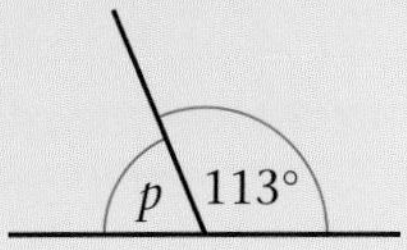

Ⓔ

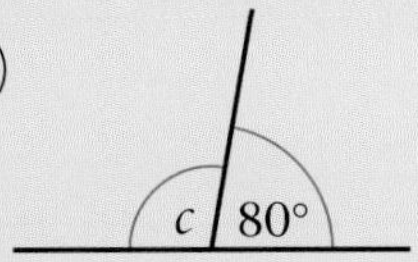

Calculate the missing angles.

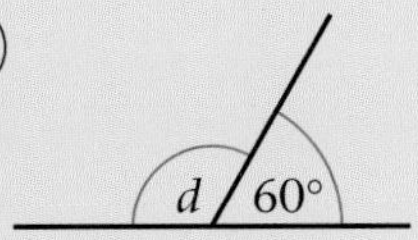

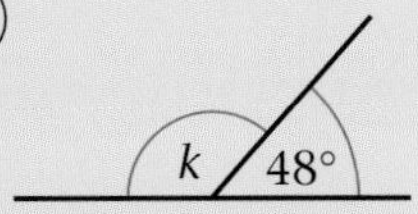

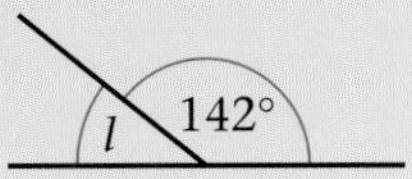

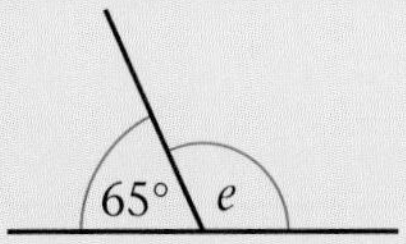

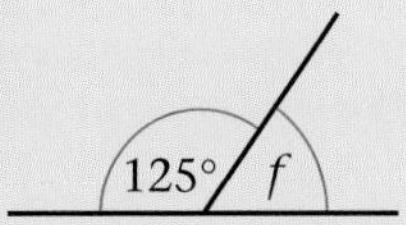

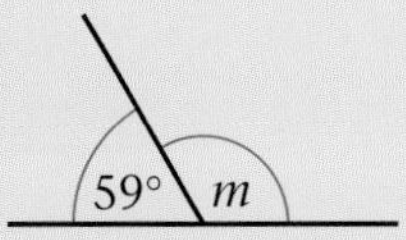

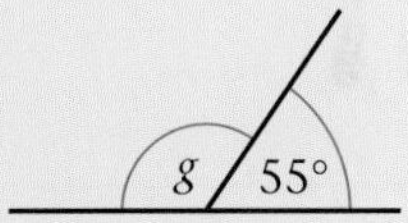

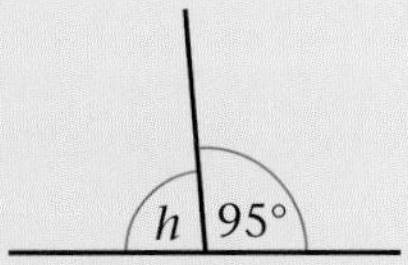

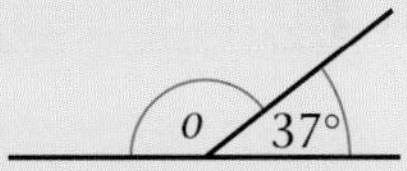

① 60° 80° q

③ 64° s 70°

⑤ 40° u 50°

⑦ 68° 72° w

② r 90° 37°

④ t 83° 50°

⑥ 80° v 80°

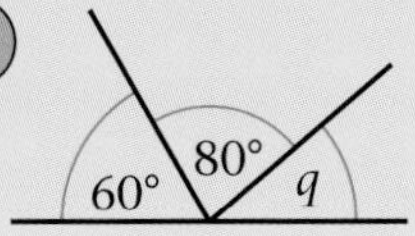

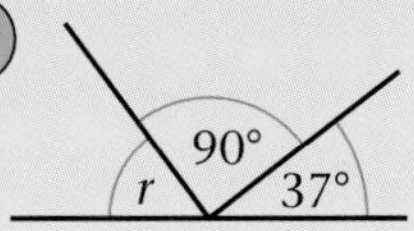

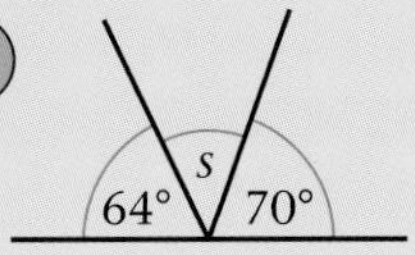

⑧ 95° x 33°

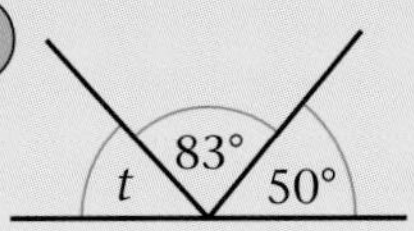

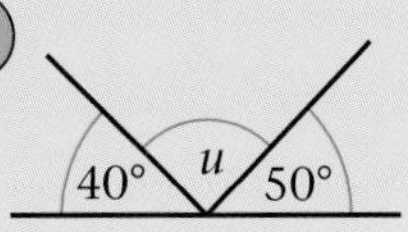

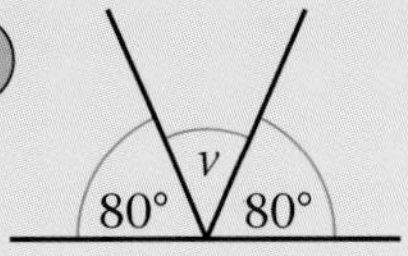

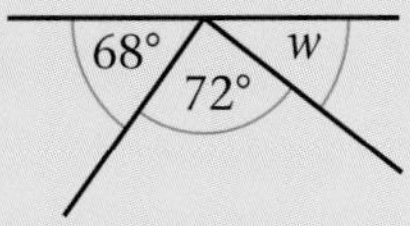

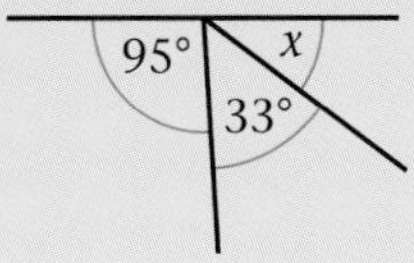

On these pages you will learn that the angles in a triangle add up to 180°
and that the angles around a point add up to 360°.

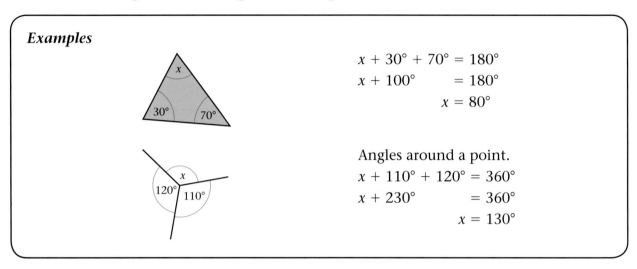

Examples

$$x + 30° + 70° = 180°$$
$$x + 100°\qquad = 180°$$
$$x = 80°$$

Angles around a point.
$$x + 110° + 120° = 360°$$
$$x + 230°\qquad\quad = 360°$$
$$x = 130°$$

Ⓜ

Calculate the missing angles.

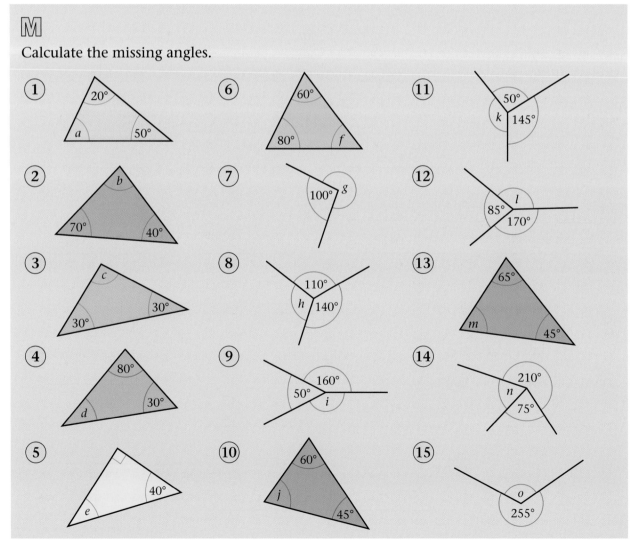

E

Calculate the missing angles.

1

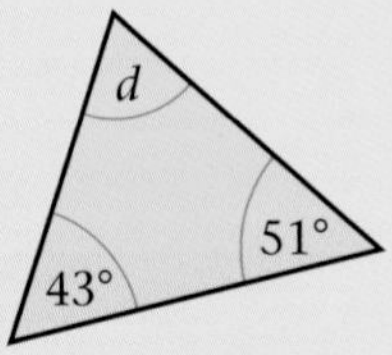

d 51°   43°

2

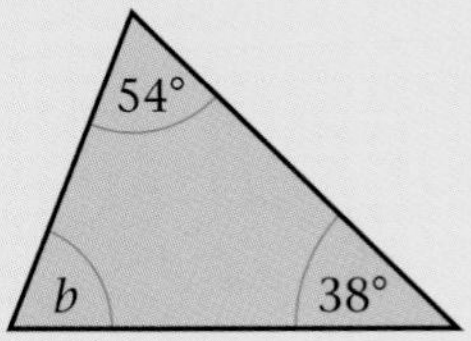

54° b 38°

3

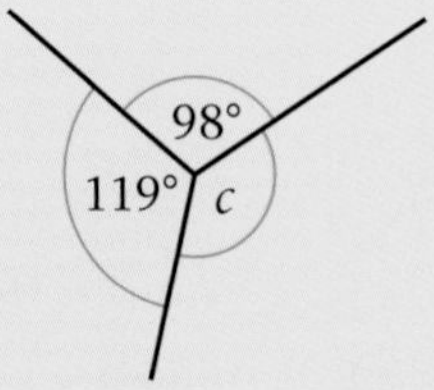

98°   119° c

4

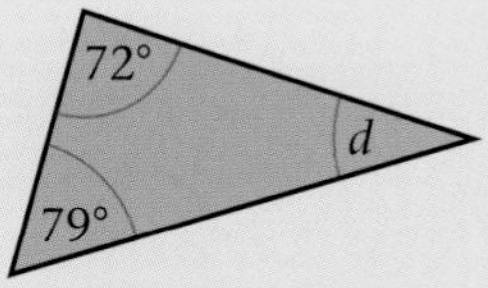

72°   79° d

5

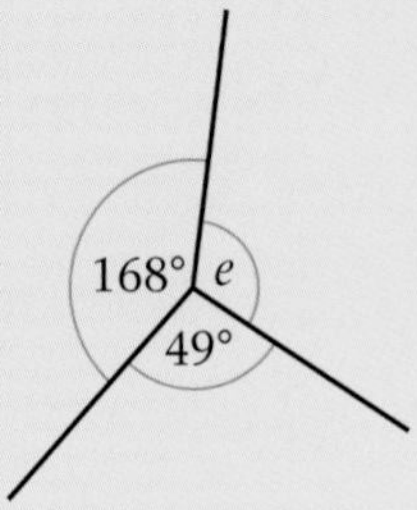

168° e 49°

6

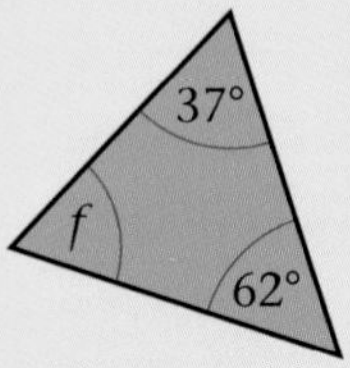

37° f 62°

7

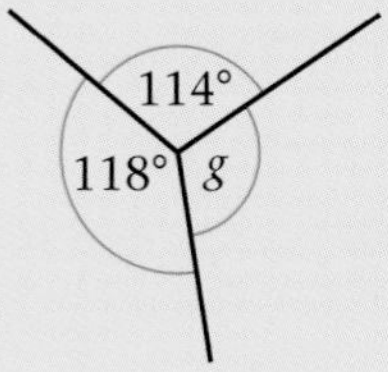

114°   118° g

8

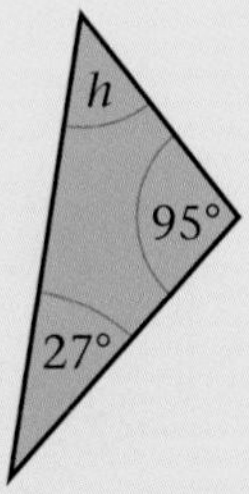

h 95°   27°

9

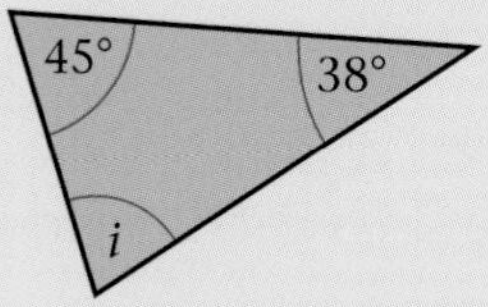

45°   38° i

10

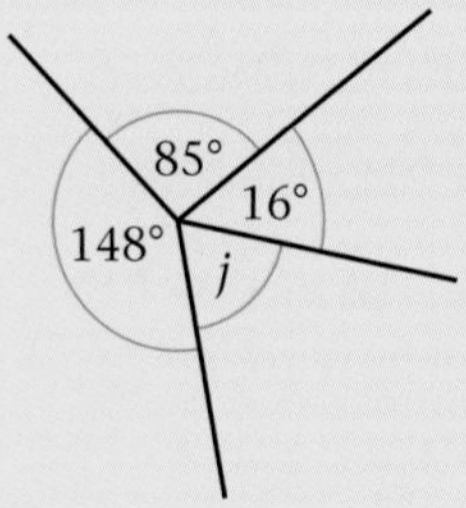

85°   16°   148° j

11

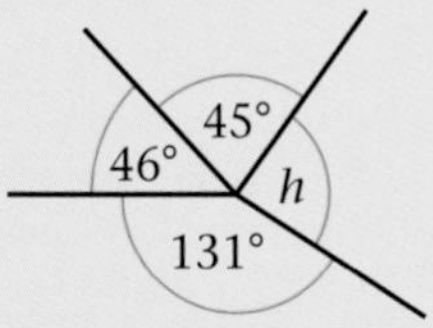

45°   46° h 131°

12

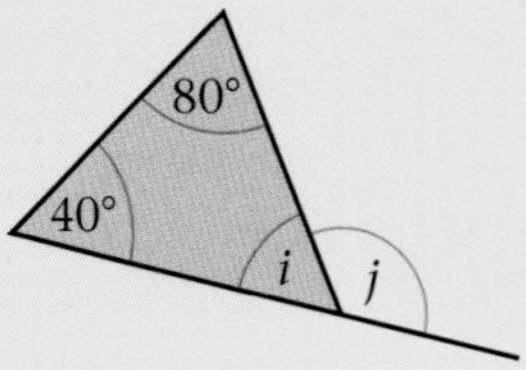

80°   40° i j

13

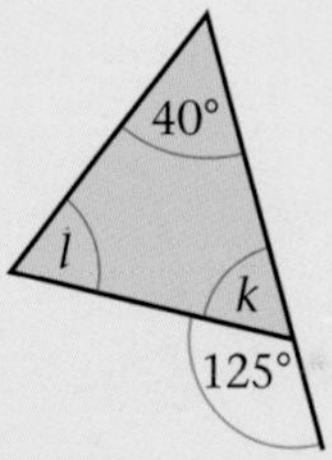

40° l k 125°

14

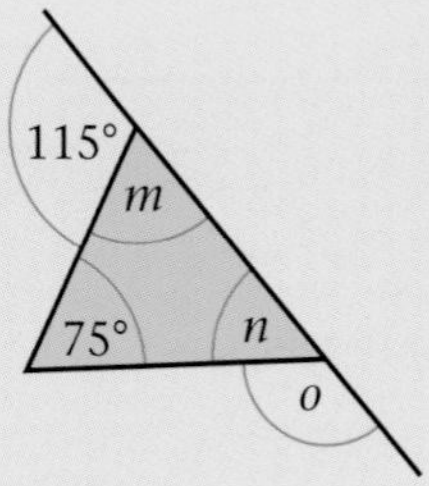

115° m 75° n o

15

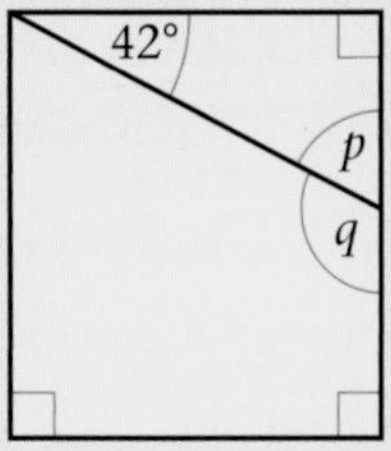

42° p q

On these pages you will learn about fractions.

If a cake is shared equally between 4 people
(or divided into 4), each person would get
$\frac{1}{4}$ of the cake.

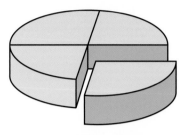

If the same cake is shared between 3 people,
each person would get $\frac{1}{3}$ of the cake.
[one whole ÷ 3 = $\frac{1}{3}$]

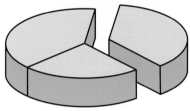

If two of these cakes were each divided equally into 3 and each person was given one
piece from each cake, they would each have $\frac{2}{3}$ of *one whole cake*.

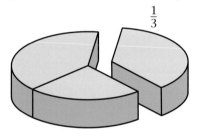 $\frac{1}{3}$

\+

$\frac{2}{3}$

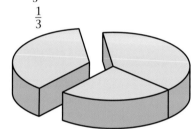 $\frac{1}{3}$

So a fraction $\frac{2}{3}$
means 2 divided
by 3.

Ⓜ

①   What fraction of one whole cake does each person get if
    a)   one cake is divided equally into 6 pieces
    b)   one cake is divided equally into 5 pieces
    c)   one cake is divided equally into 8 pieces
    d)   one cake is divided equally into 7 pieces
    e)   one cake is divided equally into 10 pieces
    f)   one cake is divided equally into 12 pieces.

②   What fraction of one whole cake do you get if
    a)   one cake is divided equally into 4 pieces and you are given 3 pieces
    b)   one cake is divided equally into 5 pieces and you are given 2 pieces
    c)   one cake is divided equally into 6 pieces and you are given 5 pieces
    d)   one cake is divided equally into 7 pieces and you are given 3 pieces
    e)   one cake is divided equally into 8 pieces and you are given 3 pieces
    f)   one cake is divided equally into 10 pieces and you are given 7 pieces.

3 For each shape, below, what fraction has been shaded?

a)

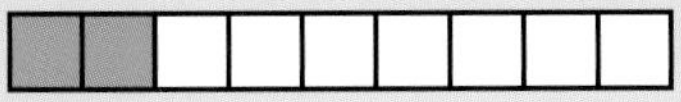

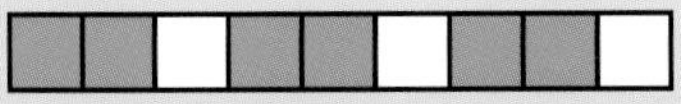

g)

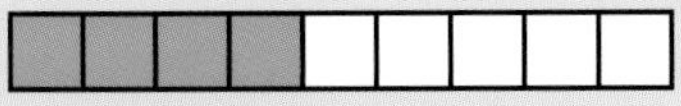

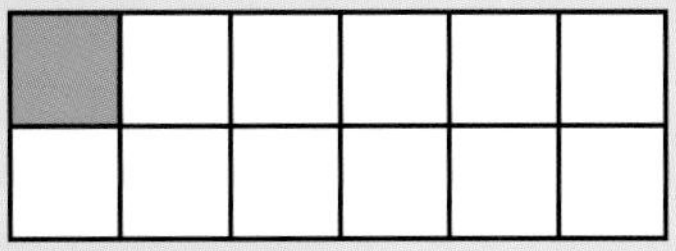

b)

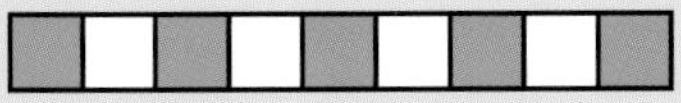

h)

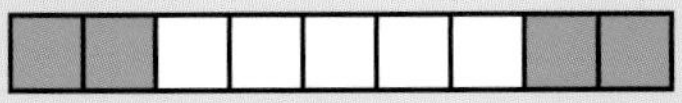

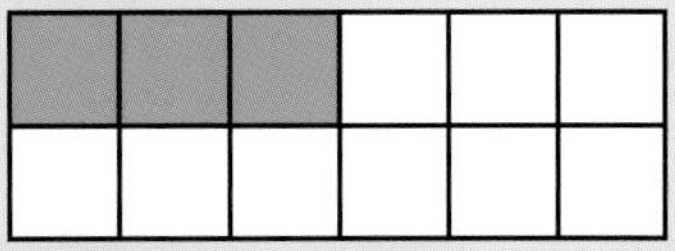

c)

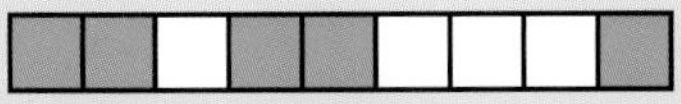

i)

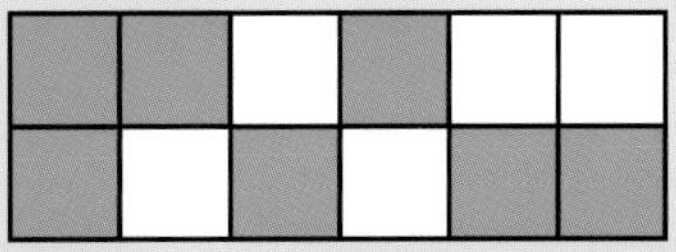

d)

j)

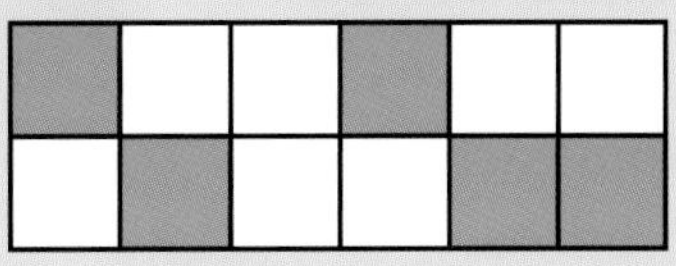

e)

k)

f)

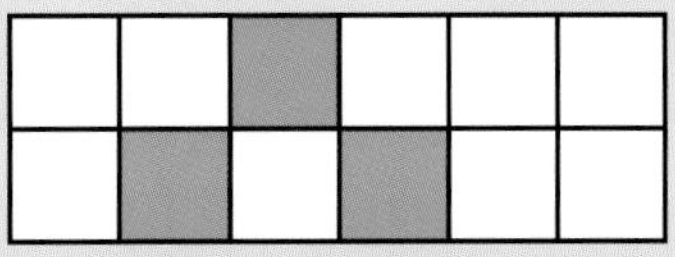

l)

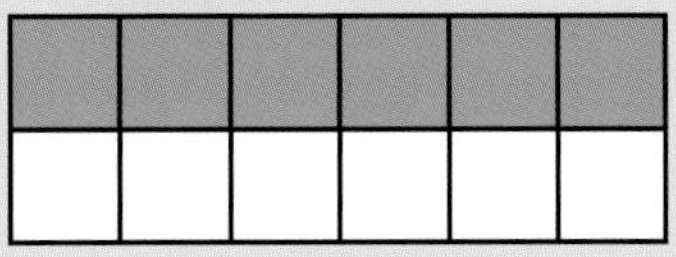

4 Write each division as a fraction:

a) $2 \div 7$ f) $7 \div 10$ k) $7 \div 12$
b) $3 \div 5$ g) $6 \div 11$ l) $5 \div 7$
c) $4 \div 9$ h) $1 \div 11$ m) $7 \div 8$
d) $4 \div 5$ i) $5 \div 6$ n) $15 \div 19$
e) $7 \div 9$ j) $3 \div 8$ o) $17 \div 100$

E

1 A 'Raynerone' chocolate bar has 11 small equal squares.

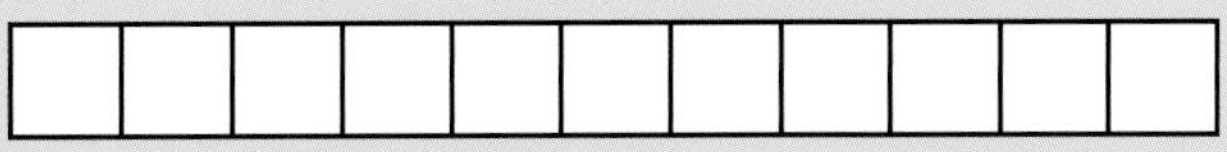

What fraction of the bar would you have if you are given

a) 5 squares   b) 7 squares   c) 3 squares
d) 6 squares   e) 4 squares?

2 If two 'Raynerone' chocolate bars are broken into squares, what fraction of *one* whole bar would you have if you are given

a) one square from each   b) three squares from each
c) five squares from each   d) two squares from each?

3 'Gibson' milk chocolate bars are made of better chocolate but only have 7 small equal squares.

What fraction of the bar would you have if you are given
a) 2 squares
b) 5 squares
c) 6 squares
d) 3 squares
e) 4 squares?

4 If two 'Gibson' milk chocolate bars are broken into squares, what fraction of one whole bar would you have if you are given
a) one square from each
b) two squares from each
c) three squares from each
d) one square from one bar and 2 from the other bar
e) one square from one bar and 3 from the other bar
f) one square from one bar and 4 from the other bar
g) two squares from one bar and 3 from the other bar
h) two squares from one bar and 4 from the other bar?

5 'BLANCO' chocolate bars are made from best quality white chocolate and have 13 small equal squares.

What fraction of the bar would you have if you were given
a) 3 squares
b) 7 squares
c) 4 squares
d) 9 squares
e) 8 squares?

6 If 2 'BLANCO' chocolate bars are broken into squares, what fraction of one whole bar do you have if you are given
a) one square from each
b) two squares from each
c) three squares from each
d) four squares from each
e) one square from the first bar and two from the second bar
f) two squares from the first bar and six from the second bar
g) two squares from the first bar and three from the second bar
h) three squares from the first bar and four from the second bar?

On this page you will learn to find a fraction of a number or quantity.

Examples

$\frac{1}{5}$ of 30 = 30 ÷ 5
= 6

$\frac{3}{10}$ of 40 = (40 ÷ 10) × 3.
= 4 × 3
= 12

What fraction of £1 is 5p?
Twenty 5p's make £1.
5p is $\frac{1}{20}$ of £1.

M Part 1

Find $\frac{1}{2}$ of:

(1) 12   (6) 16
(2) 24   (7) 30
(3) 18p   (8) 60p
(4) 40p   (9) 28p
(5) 100 cm   (10) 50 cm.

Find $\frac{1}{10}$ of:

(11) 30   (16) 20
(12) 40   (17) 10
(13) 90p   (18) 70p
(14) 50p   (19) 100p
(15) 80 cm   (20) 60 cm.

Find $\frac{1}{5}$ of:

(21) 20   (26) 50
(22) 100   (27) 40
(23) 15p   (28) 35p
(24) 30p   (29) 10p
(25) 25 cm   (30) 45 cm.

(31) There are 34 fish in a pond. One half of them are gold. How many gold fish are there?

Part 2

Find

(1) $\frac{1}{2}$ of 22
(2) $\frac{1}{5}$ of 25
(3) $\frac{1}{10}$ of 80
(4) $\frac{1}{4}$ of 24
(5) $\frac{1}{3}$ of 15 cm
(6) $\frac{1}{2}$ of 1 m
(7) $\frac{1}{5}$ of £1.00
(8) $\frac{1}{10}$ of £1.00
(9) $\frac{1}{4}$ of 80p
(10) $\frac{1}{3}$ of 24p.

What fraction of:

(11) £1 is 10p?
(12) £1 is 50p?
(13) £1 is 20p?
(14) £1 is 25p?

(15) 1 m is 1 cm?
(16) 1 m is 25 cm?
(17) 1 m is 10 cm?
(18) 1 m is 50 cm?

E

Find

(1) $\frac{3}{4}$ of 28
(2) $\frac{4}{5}$ of 30
(3) $\frac{2}{3}$ of 18
(4) $\frac{7}{10}$ of 20
(5) $\frac{3}{10}$ of 500
(6) $\frac{1}{100}$ of 700
(7) $\frac{9}{10}$ of 1 m
(8) $\frac{32}{100}$ of 1 m
(9) $\frac{6}{10}$ of 50p
(10) $\frac{51}{100}$ of £1.00.

What fraction of:

(11) £2 is 50p?
(12) £2 is 10p?
(13) £5 is 50p?
(14) £5 is 10p?
(15) 2 m is 50 cm?
(16) 2 m is 10 cm?
(17) 4 m is 50 cm?
(18) 4 m is 10 cm?

(19) There are 28 children in a class. Five sevenths of the children do not use a pen. How many of the children *do* use a pen?

(20) There are 12 eggs in a box. Two thirds of them are broken. How many eggs are unbroken?

On these pages you will learn to recognise equivalent fractions and decimals.

It is important to remember that:

$\frac{1}{10} = 0.1$ $\frac{2}{10} = 0.2$ $\frac{3}{10} = 0.3$ $\frac{1}{2} = 0.5$ $\frac{1}{4} = 0.25$ $\frac{3}{4} = 0.75$ and so on

Ⓜ **Part 1**

Copy and complete by writing a decimal in the box.

① $\frac{1}{10} = \square$ ④ $\frac{3}{10} = \square$

② $\frac{1}{4} = \square$ ⑤ $\frac{3}{4} = \square$

③ $\frac{1}{2} = \square$ ⑥ $\frac{6}{10} = \square$

Write the larger amount of money from each pair.

⑦ 12p   £0.20

⑧ 77p   £0.70

⑨ 41p   £0.40

⑩ £0.13   8p

⑪ £0.90   99p

⑫ £0.07   50p

⑬ Match each fraction with one of the decimals.

$\frac{1}{2}$	0.25
$\frac{1}{10}$	0.4
$\frac{7}{10}$	0.1
$\frac{3}{4}$	0.5
$\frac{1}{4}$	0.7
$\frac{4}{10}$	0.75

Part 2

Write as fractions.

① 0.4   ③ 0.1   ⑤ 0.25

② 0.5   ④ 0.6   ⑥ 0.3

Write as decimals.

⑦ £$\frac{7}{10}$ ⑩ $\frac{1}{2}$ cm

⑧ £$\frac{1}{10}$ ⑪ $\frac{8}{10}$ m

⑨ £$\frac{3}{4}$ ⑫ $\frac{2}{10}$ m

Copy and complete by writing >, < or = in the box.

⑬ $\frac{1}{2}$ $\square$ 0.2

⑭ $\frac{1}{4}$ $\square$ 0.4

⑮ $\frac{3}{4}$ $\square$ 0.3

⑯ $\frac{9}{10}$ $\square$ 0.9

⑰ Copy and complete the table.

Decimals	Fractions
	$\frac{3}{10}$
	$\frac{9}{10}$
	$\frac{1}{2}$
	$\frac{10}{10}$
	$\frac{1}{4}$
0.2	
0.7	
0.75	
0.1	

Write as whole numbers and fractions.

(Example 3·25 = $3\frac{1}{4}$)

① 1·5 **⑤** 4·9 **⑨** 6·82

② 3·8 **⑥** 11·6 **⑩** 8·75

③ 7·3 **⑦** 5·25 **⑪** 13·14

④ 2·7 **⑧** 17·43 **⑫** 20·09

$\frac{1}{4}$ m   0.25 m

Write as decimals.

⑬ $1\frac{1}{2}$ **⑰** $2\frac{8}{10}$ **㉑** £$\frac{72}{100}$

⑭ $3\frac{7}{10}$ **⑱** $2\frac{3}{4}$ **㉒** $1\frac{3}{4}$ m

⑮ $4\frac{1}{4}$ **⑲** £$6\frac{9}{10}$ **㉓** $5\frac{3}{10}$ cm

⑯ $9\frac{4}{10}$ **⑳** £$3\frac{1}{2}$ **㉔** $\frac{73}{100}$ m

Express each shaded area as:

a) a fraction

b) a decimal

c) a percentage.

㉕   **㉖**   **㉗**   **㉘**

㉙   **㉚**   **㉛**   **㉜**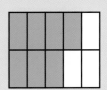

㉝ 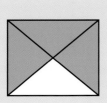   **㉞**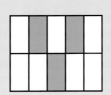

On this page you will solve simple problems involving ratio and proportion.

Ⓜ

① In a Lucky Dip 1 ticket in every 5 wins a prize.
Copy and complete the table.

Number of tickets	5									
Number of prizes	1	2	3	4	5	6	7	8	9	10

② Make a similar table for a Lucky Dip in which 1 ticket in every 4 wins a prize.

Copy and complete these sentences for each of the patterns below.
Write both sentences for each pattern.

③ ☐☐☐☐☐☐☐   ④ ☐☐☐☐☐☐☐☐☐   ⑤ ☐☐☐☐☐

a) 1 in every ☐ squares is yellow.

b) There are ☐ white squares to every 1 yellow square.

Draw a tile pattern like those above in which:

⑥ 1 in every 5 squares is shaded.

⑦ There are 3 white squares to every shaded square.

⑧ 1 in every 3 squares is shaded.

Ⓔ

① At the Chess Club there is one girl for every three boys.
There are 4 girls at the club. How many boys are there?

② Kylie has four times as many sweets as Jade.
Jade has 8 sweets. How many sweets does Kylie have?

③ Two in every three people watching a film are children.
There are 150 people in the cinema. How many are adults?

④ Josh has read half as many pages of his book as Brandon. Brandon has read 62 pages.
How many pages has Josh read?

⑤ There are five red marbles for every 2 green marbles in a jar.
There are 25 red marbles in the jar. How many green marbles are there?

⑥ Three in every seven ice creams sold are vanilla flavour. 21 vanilla ice creams are
sold. How many ice creams are sold altogether?

On this page you will practise again how to change an improper fraction to a mixed number and vice-versa.

Example: $= 3\frac{1}{4}$

M

Write the shaded areas as both mixed numbers and improper fractions.

1. $= 2\frac{2}{3} = \frac{8}{3}$

2.

3.

4.

5.

6.

7.

8.

9.

10.

Copy and complete.

11. $3\frac{1}{3} = \frac{10}{\square}$

12. $4\frac{1}{2} = \frac{9}{\square}$

13. $2\frac{7}{10} = \frac{\square}{10}$

14. $3\frac{1}{4} = \frac{\square}{4}$

15. $1\frac{2}{3} = \frac{\square}{\square}$

16. $\frac{7}{3} = 2\frac{\square}{3}$

17. $\frac{5}{4} = \square\frac{1}{4}$

18. $\frac{9}{5} = \square\frac{\square}{5}$

19. $\frac{11}{4} = \square\frac{\square}{4}$

20. $\frac{23}{6} = \square\frac{\square}{\square}$

E

Change to mixed numbers.

1. $\frac{18}{5}$

2. $\frac{21}{4}$

3. $\frac{25}{6}$

4. $\frac{17}{5}$

5. $\frac{31}{4}$

6. $\frac{19}{4}$

7. $\frac{20}{3}$

8. $\frac{32}{5}$

9. $\frac{34}{7}$

10. $\frac{41}{7}$

11. $\frac{39}{8}$

12. $\frac{50}{10}$

13. $\frac{27}{3}$

14. $\frac{62}{10}$

15. $\frac{53}{10}$

16. $\frac{84}{9}$

Change to improper fractions.

17. $3\frac{2}{5}$

18. $5\frac{3}{4}$

19. $4\frac{2}{3}$

20. $6\frac{2}{5}$

21. $5\frac{3}{5}$

22. $4\frac{2}{9}$

23. $4\frac{3}{8}$

24. $5\frac{4}{5}$

25. $6\frac{2}{3}$

26. $3\frac{4}{7}$

27. $3\frac{1}{8}$

28. $7\frac{5}{6}$

29. $10\frac{3}{10}$

30. $8\frac{5}{7}$

On this page you will use your knowledge of equivalent fractions to compare and order fractions.

Example

Place $\frac{5}{6}$, $\frac{1}{3}$, $\frac{1}{2}$ in order, smallest first.

Get the denominator the same for each fraction:

$$\overset{\times 2}{\frac{1}{3} = \frac{2}{6}} \qquad \overset{\times 3}{\frac{1}{2} = \frac{3}{6}} \qquad \text{Leave } \frac{5}{6}$$
$$\underset{\times 2}{} \qquad \underset{\times 3}{}$$

Arrange in order: $\frac{2}{6}$, $\frac{3}{6}$, $\frac{5}{6}$

$\downarrow$ $\downarrow$ $\downarrow$

$\frac{1}{3}$, $\frac{1}{2}$, $\frac{5}{6}$

Ⓜ

① Write down the smaller fraction.

a) $\frac{3}{4}$ or $\frac{3}{8}$ d) $\frac{1}{4}$ or $\frac{3}{8}$

b) $\frac{1}{10}$ or $\frac{1}{5}$ e) $\frac{1}{4}$ or $\frac{1}{3}$

c) $\frac{1}{2}$ or $\frac{3}{8}$ f) $\frac{3}{4}$ or $\frac{2}{3}$

② Place in order, smallest first:

a) $\frac{3}{4}$, $\frac{1}{2}$, $\frac{3}{8}$

b) $\frac{1}{3}$, $\frac{1}{2}$, $\frac{1}{6}$

c) $\frac{3}{5}$, $\frac{1}{2}$, $\frac{7}{10}$

d) 2, $2\frac{3}{4}$, $1\frac{3}{4}$, $2\frac{1}{2}$, $1\frac{1}{2}$

e) $3\frac{1}{4}$, 3, $3\frac{1}{2}$, $2\frac{3}{4}$, $3\frac{3}{4}$

Ⓔ

① Place in order, smallest first:

a) $\frac{11}{16}$, $\frac{3}{4}$, $\frac{5}{8}$

b) $\frac{2}{3}$, $\frac{5}{6}$, $\frac{9}{12}$

c) $\frac{2}{5}$, $\frac{5}{10}$, $\frac{9}{20}$

d) $5\frac{1}{4}$, $5\frac{2}{3}$, 5, $5\frac{1}{2}$

e) $1\frac{1}{5}$, $1\frac{1}{4}$, $1\frac{1}{8}$, 1

② Match the fractions to the letters:

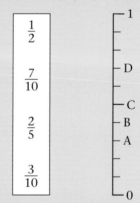

③ Match the fractions to the letters:

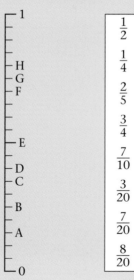

On this page you will learn to find percentages of numbers.

Examples

25% of 36 = $\frac{1}{4}$ of 36
         = 9

30% of £1 = $\frac{3}{10}$ of £1
         = 30p

Examples

Find 75% of £500.

100% of £500 = £500
50% of £500 = £250
25% of £500 = £125
75% of £500 = £375

M

Find 10% of:

(1) 30 (4) 40
(2) 90 (5) 100
(3) 60 (6) 70.

Find 50% of:

(7) 18 (10) 200
(8) 50 (11) 48
(9) 42 (12) 70.

Find 25% of:

(13) 16 (16) 100
(14) 40 (17) 32
(15) 24 (18) 200.

Find 20% of:

(19) 20 (22) 50
(20) 30 (23) 60
(21) 100 (24) 150.

Work out 25% of the following amounts of money by halving.

(25) £12·00 (28) £8·80
(26) 36p (29) 64p
(27) 80p (30) £1·60

E

Work out

(1) 10% of 60 (9) 50% of £3·00
(2) 50% of 36 (10) 20% of 15p
(3) 25% of 48 (11) 10% of £1·40
(4) 20% of 45 (12) 25% of £1·20

(5) 30% of 120 (13) 30% of £2·20
(6) 10% of 200 (14) 75% of £5·00
(7) 75% of 40 (15) 40% of £1·50
(8) 40% of 80 (16) 40% of £3·30

Work out 75% of the following amounts of money by halving.

(17) £200 (20) 48p
(18) 60p (21) £36·00
(29) £2·80 (22) 84p

(23) A pair of slippers usually cost £28.
In a sale the price is reduced by 25%.

How much do they cost now?

On these pages you will practise doubling and halving.

Examples

Double 35   = Double 30 + Double 5 = 60 + 10 = 70

Double 350   = Double 300 + Double 50 = 600 + 100 = 700

Half of 90   = Half of 100 − Half of 10 = 50 − 5 = 45

Half of 900   = Half of 800 + Half of 100 = 400 + 50 = 450

● use doubling and halving to solve calculations.

Examples

Find the 6 × table by doubling the 3 × table.

3s		6s
3	×1	6
6	×2	12
9	×3	18
and so on		

Work out multiples of 15 by doubling.

$1 \times 15 = 15$

$2 \times 15 = 30$

$4 \times 15 = 60$

$8 \times 15 = 120$

$16 \times 15 = 240$

Find quarters and eighths by halving.

$\frac{1}{2}$ of 280 = 140

$\frac{1}{4}$ of 280 = 70

$\frac{1}{8}$ of 280 = 35

Ⓜ

Double these numbers.   Halve these numbers.

① 450   ⑤ 20   ⑨ 45   ⑬ 700   ⑰ 68   ㉑ 170

② 16   ⑥ 1000   ⑩ 75   ⑭ 130   ⑱ 380   ㉒ 26

③ 55   ⑦ 85   ⑪ 150   ⑮ 260   ⑲ 600   ㉓ 800

④ 250   ⑧ 500   ⑫ 19   ⑯ 800   ⑳ 34   ㉔ 190

㉕ Work out the 6× table by doubling the 3× table.

㉖ Work out the 8× table by doubling the 4× table.

㉗ Find one quarter of:

a) 120   e) 160

b) 600   f) 36

c) 24   g) 200

d) 1000   h) 28.

28 Copy and complete by doubling.

a) $1 \times 20 = \square$ b) $1 \times 75 = \square$

     $2 \times 20 = \square$ $2 \times 75 = \square$

     $4 \times 20 = \square$ $4 \times 75 = \square$

     $8 \times 20 = \square$ $8 \times 75 = \square$

   $16 \times 20 = \square$ $16 \times 75 = \square$

29 On Monday Mr Gibson received 65 bills.

On Tuesday he received twice as many as on Monday.

On Wednesday he received twice as many as on Tuesday.

a)   How many bills did he get on Tuesday?

b)   How many bills did he get on Wednesday?

E

Double these numbers.

1 26	**5** 470	**9** 3500	**13** 34	**17** 270	**21** 4400
2 320	**6** 2400	**10** 29	**14** 450	**18** 3300	**22** 49
3 5000	**7** 58	**11** 360	**15** 2800	**19** 38	**23** 430
4 37	**8** 230	**12** 4600	**16** 44	**20** 310	**24** 3900

Find $\frac{1}{2}$ of: Find $\frac{1}{4}$ of: Find $\frac{1}{8}$ of:

25 26	**29** 920	**33** 52	**37** 960	**41** 72	**45** 400
26 580	**30** 5200	**34** 5600	**38** 84	**42** 1200	**46** 56
27 7600	**31** 740	**35** 76	**39** 6800	**43** 640	**47** 3600
28 54	**32** 94.	**36** 720	**40** 92.	**44** 96	**48** 480.

49 Work out the 12 times table by doubling the 6 times table.

50 Work out the 16 times table by doubling the 8 times table.

51 Work out multiples of 13 up to 16×13. Use your answers to work out.

a) 9×13 b) 24×13 c) 7×13 d) 18×13 e) 27×13

On this page you will learn to multiply by partitioning.

Examples $53 \times 6 = (50 \times 6) + (3 \times 6)$ $29 \times 5 = (20 \times 5) + (9 \times 5)$
$= 300 + 18$ $= 100 + 45$
$= 318$ $= 145$

M

Work out

1. $13 \times 3 = (10 \times 3) + (3 \times 3) =$
2. $18 \times 3 = (10 \times 3) + (8 \times 3) =$
3. $24 \times 3 = (20 \times 3) + (4 \times 3) =$
4. $12 \times 4 = (10 \times 4) + (2 \times 4) =$
5. $19 \times 4 = (10 \times 4) + (9 \times 4) =$

6. $23 \times 4 = (20 \times 4) + (3 \times 4) =$
7. $29 \times 3 = (20 \times 3) + (9 \times 3) =$
8. $32 \times 3 = (30 \times 3) + (2 \times 3) =$
9. $28 \times 4 = (20 \times 4) + (8 \times 4) =$
10. $33 \times 4 = (30 \times 4) + (3 \times 4) =$

Work out

1. 12×2
2. 11×5
3. 21×4
4. 13×3

5. 14×2
6. 22×3
7. 12×4
8. 34×2

9. 12×3
10. 42×2
11. 23×3
11. 22×4

E

Work out

1. 34×4
2. 57×5
3. 42×6
4. 24×7
5. 28×8

6. 32×9
7. 47×4
8. 38×5
9. 56×6
10. 35×7

11. Graham has 37 tables. There are 8 legs on each table.

   How many legs are there altogether on the tables?

On this page you will learn to use the relationship of multiplication to division.

> Multiplication is the inverse of division.
> Knowing one × or ÷ fact means that you know 3 related facts.
>
> **Example** $6 \times 4 = 24$ $4 \times 6 = 24$
> $24 \div 6 = 4$ $24 \div 4 = 6$

Ⓜ

Copy and complete by writing the missing number in the box.

① ☐ × 3 = 21

② ☐ × 4 = 36

③ 4 × ☐ = 28

④ 5 × ☐ = 20

⑤ ☐ × 1 = 5

⑥ ☐ × 5 = 35

⑦ 6 × ☐ = 54

⑧ 7 × ☐ = 42

⑨ ☐ × 6 = 36

⑩ ☐ × 8 = 24

⑪ 8 × ☐ = 0

⑫ 9 × ☐ = 90

Write four different × or ÷ statements for each set of numbers, as in the example above.

⑬ 6, 8, 48

⑭ 8, 56, 7

⑮ 8, 9, 72

⑯ 63, 9, 7

⑰ 10, 120, 12

⑱ 54, 6, 9

Ⓔ

Copy and complete.

① ☐ × 4 = 48

② ☐ × 7 = 7

③ 3 × ☐ = 75

④ 9 × ☐ = 72

⑤ ☐ × 8 = 56

⑥ ☐ × 9 = 36

⑦ 7 × ☐ = 49

⑧ 9 × ☐ = 0

⑨ ☐ × 6 = 48

⑩ ☐ × 5 = 60

⑪ 8 × ☐ = 88

⑫ 4 × ☐ = 60

Copy and complete these multiplication squares.

⑬

×	8		
			42
4		36	
	24		21

⑭

×		7	
		21	15
			40
9	54		

⑮

×			
		54	
	40		16
	35	42	

On this page you will learn a standard method for multiplication.

Examples

$$\begin{array}{r} 1\ 3\ 4 \\ \times\quad 3 \\ \hline 4\ 0\ 2 \\ {\scriptstyle 1\ 1} \end{array}$$

$$\begin{array}{r} 2\ 1\ 5 \\ \times\quad 4 \\ \hline 8\ 6\ 0 \\ {\scriptstyle 2} \end{array}$$

$$\begin{array}{r} 4\cdot8 \\ \times\ 4 \\ \hline 19\cdot2 \\ {\scriptstyle 3} \end{array}$$

$$\begin{array}{r} 5\cdot3 \\ \times\ 6 \\ \hline 31\cdot8 \\ {\scriptstyle 1} \end{array}$$

M

Work out.

1. $\begin{array}{r} 176 \\ \times\ 5 \\ \hline \end{array}$

2. $\begin{array}{r} 258 \\ \times\ 7 \\ \hline \end{array}$

3. $\begin{array}{r} 249 \\ \times\ 6 \\ \hline \end{array}$

4. $\begin{array}{r} 346 \\ \times\ 9 \\ \hline \end{array}$

5. $\begin{array}{r} 239 \\ \times\ 8 \\ \hline \end{array}$

6. $\begin{array}{r} 386 \\ \times\ 4 \\ \hline \end{array}$

7. $\begin{array}{r} 658 \\ \times\ 7 \\ \hline \end{array}$

8. $\begin{array}{r} 549 \\ \times\ 3 \\ \hline \end{array}$

9. $\begin{array}{r} 167 \\ \times\ 3 \\ \hline \end{array}$

10. $\begin{array}{r} 257 \\ \times\ 6 \\ \hline \end{array}$

11. $\begin{array}{r} 135 \\ \times\ 9 \\ \hline \end{array}$

12. $\begin{array}{r} 329 \\ \times\ 7 \\ \hline \end{array}$

13. $\begin{array}{r} 456 \\ \times\ 8 \\ \hline \end{array}$

14. $\begin{array}{r} 348 \\ \times\ 7 \\ \hline \end{array}$

15. $\begin{array}{r} 829 \\ \times\ 5 \\ \hline \end{array}$

16. $\begin{array}{r} 289 \\ \times\ 8 \\ \hline \end{array}$

E

Work out.

1. $\begin{array}{r} 4\cdot3 \\ \times\ 2 \\ \hline \end{array}$

2. $\begin{array}{r} 5\cdot2 \\ \times\ 3 \\ \hline \end{array}$

3. $\begin{array}{r} 6\cdot9 \\ \times\ 4 \\ \hline \end{array}$

4. $\begin{array}{r} 4\cdot8 \\ \times\ 5 \\ \hline \end{array}$

5. $\begin{array}{r} 9\cdot7 \\ \times\ 3 \\ \hline \end{array}$

6. $\begin{array}{r} 4\cdot2 \\ \times\ 6 \\ \hline \end{array}$

7. Wayne bought 4 packets each weighing 2·3 kg.
   How much did they weigh altogether?

8. $7\cdot9 \times 3$

9. $4\cdot3 \times 6$

10. $9\cdot8 \times 2$

11. $8\cdot2 \times 7$

12. $2\cdot7 \times 9$

13. $4\cdot3 \times 8$

On this page you will learn to use a standard written method for division.

Examples

$96 \div 6$

$$
\begin{array}{r}
6\overline{)96} \\
-60 \quad (10 \times 6) \\
\hline
36 \\
36 \quad (6 \times 6) \\
\hline
0
\end{array}
$$

Answer 16

$196 \div 6$

$$
\begin{array}{r}
6\overline{)196} \\
-180 \quad (30 \times 6) \\
\hline
16 \\
12 \quad (2 \times 6) \\
\hline
4
\end{array}
$$

Answer 32 remainder 4

You may find it useful to check your answer with the inverse operation.
Example $96 \div 6 = 16$

$$
\begin{array}{r}
16 \\
\times \ 6 \\
\hline
96 \\
\hline
3
\end{array}
$$

M

Work out

1. $36 \div 2$
2. $95 \div 5$
3. $96 \div 6$
4. $98 \div 7$

5. $69 \div 3$
6. $96 \div 8$
7. $136 \div 4$
8. $126 \div 9$

9. $120 \div 5$
10. $108 \div 6$
11. $102 \div 3$
12. $136 \div 8$

13. $112 \div 4$
14. $153 \div 9$
15. $145 \div 5$
16. $154 \div 7$

17. Carrots are sold in packets of 8. How many packets are made up from 168 carrots?

18. 150 children are divided equally into 6 classes. How many children are there in each class?

19. A school buys 180 pencils. One quarter of the pencils are used. How many are left?

E

Work out

1. $114 \div 6$
2. $147 \div 7$
3. $176 \div 8$
4. $162 \div 9$

5. $126 \div 6$
6. $105 \div 7$
7. $149 \div 8$
8. $225 \div 9$

9. $162 \div 6$
10. $161 \div 7$
11. $232 \div 8$
12. $198 \div 9$

13. $144 \div 6$
14. $217 \div 7$
15. $191 \div 8$
16. $306 \div 9$

17. A packet of sweets weighs 224 g. Each sweet weighs 8 g. How many sweets are there in the packet?

18. 7 oil drums contain 315 litres. How much oil is there in each drum?

19. One seventh of the 308 children in a school come by bus. How many children come to school in other ways?

On this page you will practise more long multiplication (2 digit by 2 digit numbers).

M

Work out.

1.   23
   × 14
   ⎯⎯

2.   31
   × 24
   ⎯⎯

3.   22
   × 15
   ⎯⎯

4.   14
   × 13
   ⎯⎯

5. 13 × 31

6. 21 × 25

7. 42 × 25

8. 45 × 22

9. 33 × 13

10. 43 × 30

11. There are 52 cards in a pack. How many cards are there in 31 packs?

E

Work out.

1. 38 × 66

2. 87 × 72

3. 64 × 47

4. 69 × 94

5. 57 × 89

6. 84 × 52

7. 76 × 94

8. Rachel earns £85 each week for 38 weeks.
   How much does she earn in total?

9. 46 people go to a rock concert. Each ticket costs £23. What is the total cost of the tickets?

10. A tube of fruit pastilles contains 15 pastilles. If I bought 16 tubes, how many fruit pastilles would I have altogether?

On this page you will learn to use tests of divisibility.

Whole numbers are divisible by:

100 if the last two digits are 00.

10 if the last digit is 0.

2 if the number is even.

4 if the last two digits are divisible by 4.

5 if the last digit is 0 or 5.

3 if the sum of the digits is divisible by 3.

M

Write True or False for each of the following statements.

(1) 300 is divisible by 100.   (6) 58 is divisible by 5.   (11) 814 is divisible by 4.

(2) 61 is divisible by 2.   (7) 32 is divisible by 2.   (12) 200 is divisible by 10.

(3) 320 is divisible by 5.   (8) 470 is divisible by 100. (13) 50 is divisible by 100.

(4) 226 is divisible by 4.   (9) 340 is divisible by 4.   (14) 45 is divisible by 2.

(5) 40 is divisible by 10.   (10) 174 is divisible by 5.   (15) 136 is divisible by 4.

Write down which of these numbers is divisible by:

(16) 100	(17) 10	(18) 2	(19) 4	(20) 5
600	70	18	68	65
4040	65	94	422	312
320	900	247	784	830
1000	1320	1356	978	715
750	836	865	236	964

E

Copy and complete the table, using ticks and crosses to show divisibility.

Number	Divisible by				
	2	3	4	5	10
415	✗				
648	✓				
760					
834					
964					

On this page you will learn to use letters in place of numbers.

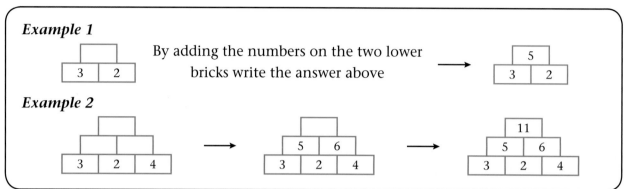

M

Fill in each empty box like the examples above.

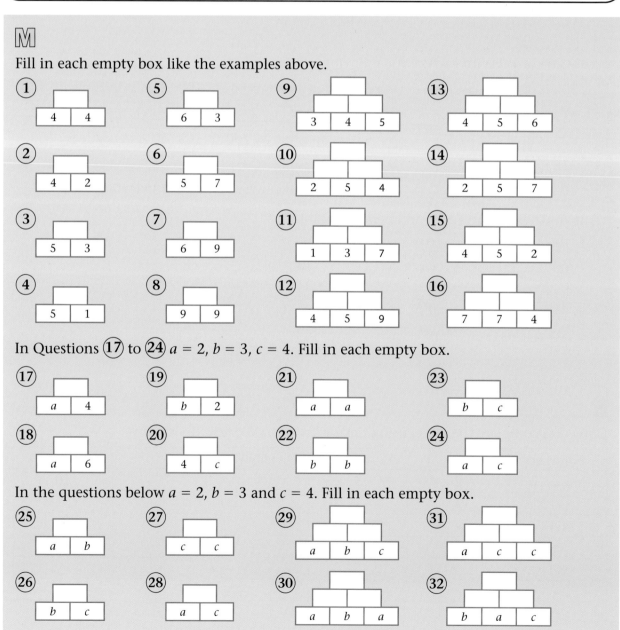

In Questions ⑰ to ㉔ $a = 2$, $b = 3$, $c = 4$. Fill in each empty box.

In the questions below $a = 2$, $b = 3$ and $c = 4$. Fill in each empty box.

Using letters only:

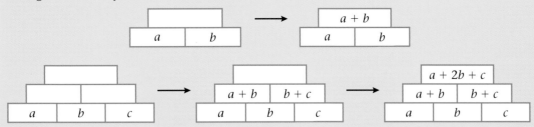

Fill in each empty box like the examples above.

①

4	4

⑥
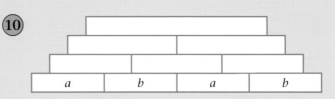

a	a	b

②

2	4

⑦
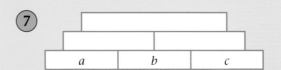

a	b	c

③

5	2

⑧

a	2a	b

④
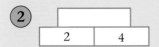

2	3	4

⑨
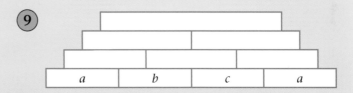

a	b	c	a

⑤
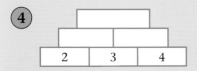

a	a	a

⑩
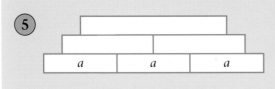

a	b	a	b

⑪ In Question **⑤**, what number is in the top box, if $a = 7$?

⑫ In Question **⑥**, what number is in the top box, if $a = 3$ and $b = 6$?

⑬ In Question **⑦**, what number is in the top box, if $a = 4$, $b = 5$ and $c = 8$?

⑭ In Question **⑧**, what number is in the top box, if $a = 4$ and $b = 9$?

⑮ In Question **⑨**, what number is in the top box, if $a = 5$, $b = 7$ and $c = 12$?

⑯ In Question **⑩**, what number is in the top box, if $a = 7$ and $b = 8$?

On this page you will use $+ - \times \div$.

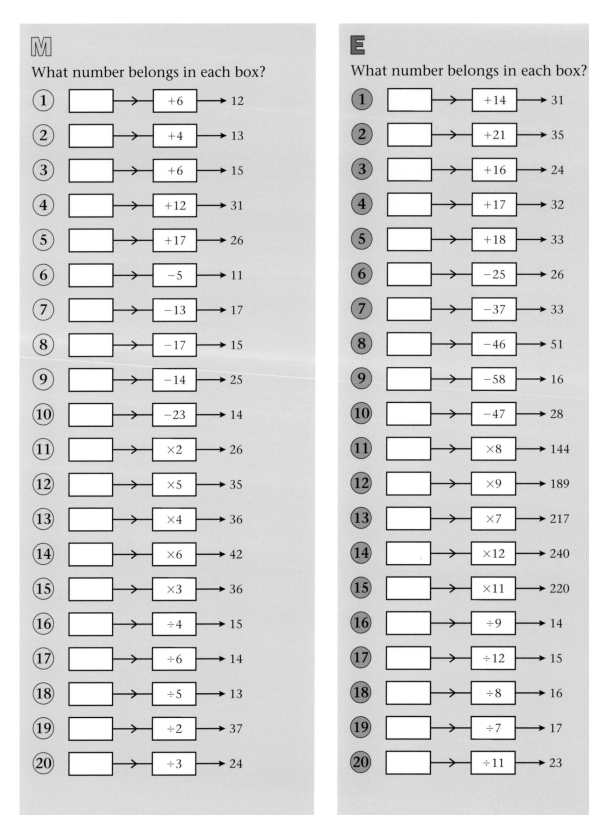

M

What number belongs in each box?

1. ⬜ → +6 → 12
2. ⬜ → +4 → 13
3. ⬜ → +6 → 15
4. ⬜ → +12 → 31
5. ⬜ → +17 → 26
6. ⬜ → −5 → 11
7. ⬜ → −13 → 17
8. ⬜ → −17 → 15
9. ⬜ → −14 → 25
10. ⬜ → −23 → 14
11. ⬜ → ×2 → 26
12. ⬜ → ×5 → 35
13. ⬜ → ×4 → 36
14. ⬜ → ×6 → 42
15. ⬜ → ×3 → 36
16. ⬜ → ÷4 → 15
17. ⬜ → ÷6 → 14
18. ⬜ → ÷5 → 13
19. ⬜ → ÷2 → 37
20. ⬜ → ÷3 → 24

E

What number belongs in each box?

1. ⬜ → +14 → 31
2. ⬜ → +21 → 35
3. ⬜ → +16 → 24
4. ⬜ → +17 → 32
5. ⬜ → +18 → 33
6. ⬜ → −25 → 26
7. ⬜ → −37 → 33
8. ⬜ → −46 → 51
9. ⬜ → −58 → 16
10. ⬜ → −47 → 28
11. ⬜ → ×8 → 144
12. ⬜ → ×9 → 189
13. ⬜ → ×7 → 217
14. ⬜ → ×12 → 240
15. ⬜ → ×11 → 220
16. ⬜ → ÷9 → 14
17. ⬜ → ÷12 → 15
18. ⬜ → ÷8 → 16
19. ⬜ → ÷7 → 17
20. ⬜ → ÷11 → 23

On this page you will learn to collect like terms.

Examples

1. $3a + 2b + 4b + a$ 2. $2a + a + a$ Beware $4a + 7$ is *not* $11a$

   $= 4a + 6b$ $= 4a$ $4a + 7$ *cannot* be simplified.

Ⓜ

Collect like terms

(1) $a + 2b + 3a$

(2) $a + 2b + a$

(3) $3a + 2b + 2a$

(4) $2a + 3b + 2b + a$

(5) $p + q + 2p$

(6) $2p + 3q + 2p + q$

(7) $3p + 4q + q + 2p$

(8) $5q + 2p + q$

(9) $5p + 2q - 2p$

(10) $x + 3y + 3x$

(11) $2x + 3x + 2y$

(12) $5x + 3y - 2x$

(13) $6f + 2n + 4f + n$

(14) $5f + 6n + f + 2n$

(15) $4f + 2n + 6f + 3n$

(16) $7r + 6s + 2r + 3s$

(17) $5r + 3s + 2r + 2s$

(18) $4r + 6r - 2r$

(19) $2a + 3a + 5b$

(20) $6x + 4y + 3y + 2x$

(21) $3a + 2b + a + 3$

(22) $4f + 2g + 2g + 6$

(23) $5x + 2y + 3x + 4$

(24) $7m + 3n - n + 2m$

(25) $7s + 3p + 2r + 3s$

(26) $4q + 2p + 3q - 2p$

(27) $2a + 3b + 2a + 4b$

(28) $3b + 2c + 4b + 3c - 2b$

(29) $3x + 4y + 6 + 2y$

(30) $4x + 2y + 3x + 2$

Ⓔ

(1) $2a + 3b + 2a + 4b$

(2) $3r + 6s - r + 2s + 4r$

(3) $10x + 7y - 3x + 4y - 2x$

(4) $17x + 10y - 4x - 3y$

(5) $18p + 17q - 10p + 4q - 5p$

(6) $8m + 16n - 4m + 2n + 5$

(7) $2p + 6q - 10p + 8q + 12p - 4q$

(8) $8p + 3q + 10p + 4q + 6q - 5p + 2$

(9) $17m + 15n + 14p - 6m + 2n - 5p$

(10) $25x + 17y - 8x + 4y + 2x - 7y$

(11) $22f + 18g + 6f + 26g - 2g$

(12) $19a + 6b - 7a + 2b - 12a - 8b + 4$

Find the perimeter of the following shapes.

(13)

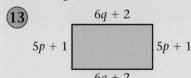

$6q + 2$

$5p + 1$ $5p + 1$

$6q + 2$

(14)

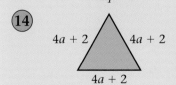

$4a + 2$ $4a + 2$

$4a + 2$

(15)

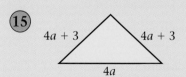

$4a + 3$ $4a + 3$

$4a$

(16)

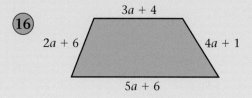

$3a + 4$

$2a + 6$ $4a + 1$

$5a + 6$

(1) Jim has 24 sweets.

Kelly ate $\frac{1}{3}$ of these sweets.
How many sweets did Kelly eat?

(2) Which of these 3 numbers is the smallest?

| $\frac{1}{4}$ | 40% | 0·4 |

(3) Work out 30% of £70

(4) Draw the reflection of the shaded shape in the mirror line.
You may use a mirror or tracing paper.

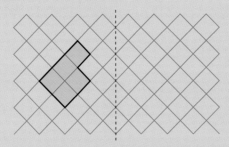

(5) $2\frac{2}{3}$ is equal to $\frac{8}{3}$

$\frac{8}{3}$ is an improper fraction.

Change $3\frac{1}{3}$ into an improper fraction.

(6) Copy this shape onto squared paper.

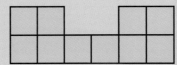

Shade $\frac{2}{5}$ of this shape.

(7) Write these fractions in order, starting with the smallest.

$$\frac{1}{3} \qquad \frac{1}{6} \qquad \frac{1}{2}$$

(8) Copy this rectangle onto squared paper.

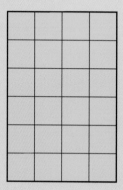

Draw on all the lines of symmetry of this rectangle.

(9) Work out 68×93

(10) At a skatepark, there are three times as many boys as girls.
If there are 9 girls, how many boys are there?

(11) Work out $154 \div 7$

(12) 138 people went to the cinema. Each person paid £6.
How much money did all the people pay in total?

(13) Copy this triangle onto squared paper.

Translate this shape by 3 squares to the right in a horizontal line.
Draw the new shape.

(14) Write down the missing number.

⑮

a) Measure this angle with a protractor.

b) What is the name of this type of angle?

⑯ Copy this diagram.

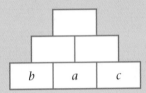

Given $a = 3$, $b = 5$ and $c = 7$, fill in each empty box by adding the numbers on the two lower bricks and writing the answer in the brick above.

⑰ Which box is the same as

$$4a + 2b + 3a + 2$$

| 11*ab* | 9*a* + 2*b* | 7*a* + 4*b* | 7*a* + 2*b* + 2 |

⑱ Annie spent 20% of her money on clothes and $\frac{1}{10}$ of her money on food. What percentage of her money did she have left?

⑲

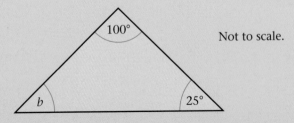

100°   Not to scale.

b   25°

Work out the size of angle *b* in the triangle above. Do **not** use a protractor (angle measurer).

On this page you will make symmetrical designs.

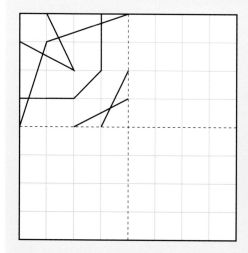

1. Copy this square and pattern onto the top left hand corner of a piece of A4 centimetre squared paper.

2. Lightly mark the reflection lines on the diagram as shown.

3. Use these lines to help you reflect the pattern across …

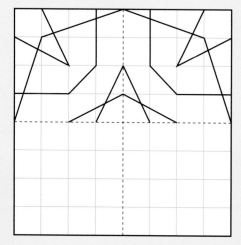

… and then down.

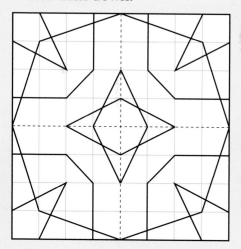

4. Repeat the process with the same tile so that your tile nearly covers the piece of paper →

5. Now colour or shade in your work as neatly and symmetrically as you can.

Reflective Symmetry 2

On this page you will learn to recognise reflective symmetry in 2-D shapes.

A shape is symmetrical if half of its shape matches the other half exactly.
The line separating the two halves is the line of symmetry or mirror line.

Examples

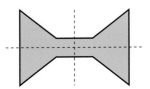

One line of symmetry   Two lines of symmetry

Which of the letters below have:

1. one line of symmetry?
2. two or more lines of symmetry?
3. no lines of symmetry?

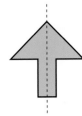

B N W H D F

X M O K R Z

7. Look at the letters above.
   Copy the letters which are
   symmetrical.
   Draw on the line(s) of symmetry.

Which of the shapes below have:

4. one line of symmetry?
5. two or more lines of symmetry?
6. no lines of symmetry?

A   B   C

D   E   F

8. Look at the shapes above.
   Use squared paper. Draw the shapes
   which are symmetrical.
   Draw on the line(s) of symmetry.

Draw three shapes with:

1. one line of symmetry.
2. two lines of symmetry.
3. more than two lines of symmetry.

Example

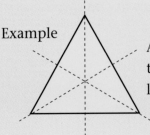

An equilateral
triangle has three
lines of symmetry

On this page you will learn to sketch the reflection of a shape in a mirror line.

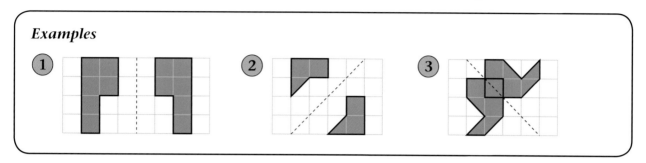

Examples

Copy the shape and the mirror line and sketch the reflection.

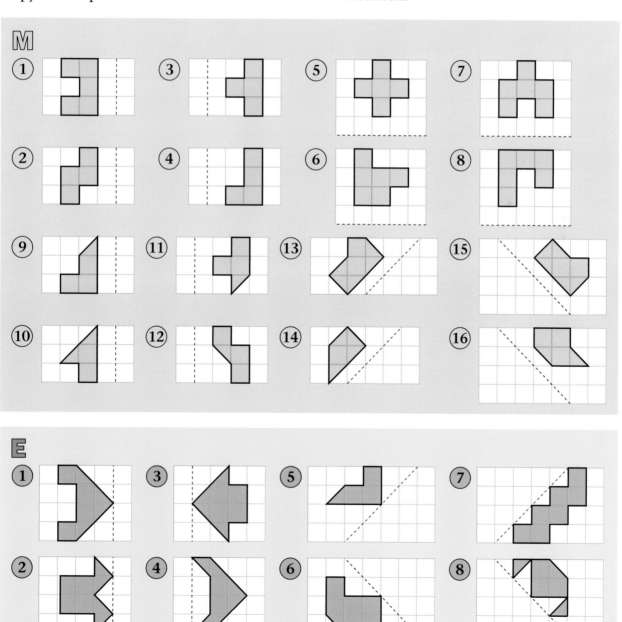

On this page you will learn to sketch the pattern of a shape after it has been translated.

Translating a shape means moving it in a straight line.

Examples Translate the shaded shape:

① left 3 squares (L3)
② up 2 squares (U2)
③ Right 2 Up 2 (R2U2)
④ Right 2 Down 1 (R2D1).

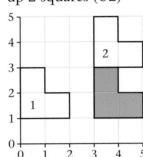

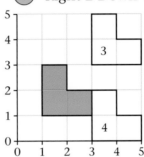

Ⓜ

Copy the grids and the shaded shapes. Translate each shape three times.

① U2
② R3
③ D2

④ L2
⑤ R2
⑥ U3

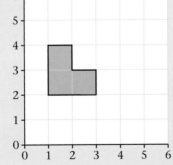

Ⓔ

① Copy the grid and the L-shaped hexagon in the first diagram in Section M above. Translate the shape three times.
   a) L1D2   **b)** R3D1   **c)** R1U2

② Copy the grid and the triangle in the second diagram in Section M above. Translate the shape three times.
   a) L1U2   **b)** R2D1   **c)** R2U3

③ Make up your own examples. Draw your own shape and then translate it two or three times.

On these pages you will look at whether shapes have rotational symmetry.

The shape B fits onto itself three times when rotated through a complete turn. It has *rotational symmetry of order three*.

The shape C fits onto itself six times when rotated through a complete turn. It has *rotational symmetry of order six*.

If a shape can only fit onto itself in its starting position, it has *rotational symmetry of order one*.

This shape has *rotational symmetry of order one*.

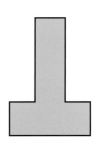

M

For each shape write down the order of rotational symmetry. (Use tracing paper)

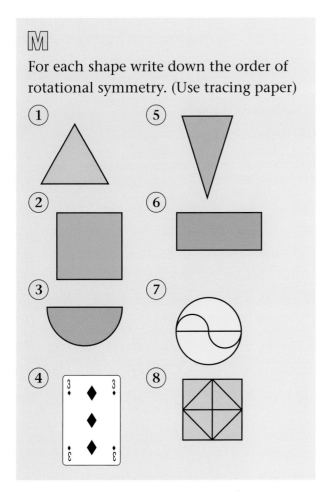

E

For each shape write down the order of rotational symmetry.

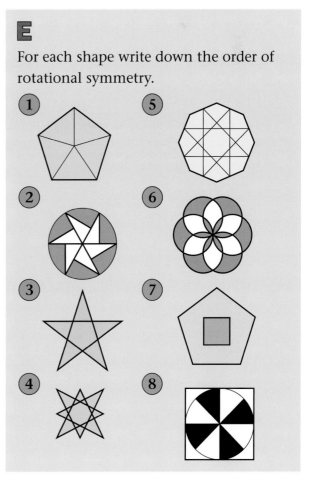

On these pages you will find the mean, median, mode and range of data.

The marks achieved by 10 pupils in a test were:
8, 5, 7, 4, 5, 6, 9, 7, 5, 10.

a) Mean mark $= \dfrac{8 + 5 + 7 + 4 + 5 + 6 + 9 + 7 + 5 + 10}{10} = \dfrac{66}{10} = 6{\cdot}6$

b) Arrange the marks in order: 4 5 5 5 6 7 7 8 9 10

$\uparrow$

the median is here

Median $= \dfrac{6 + 7}{2} = 6{\cdot}5$

c) Mode = 5, since there are more fives than any other number.

d) Range $= 10 - 4 = 6$

Ⓜ

① A fisherman caught five fish.
Their masses were 200 g, 300 g, 220 g, 190 g and 90 g.
What is the mean mass of the fish?

② In four different shops the price of one litre of lemonade
is 43p, 37p, 41p, 35p. What is the mean price of the lemonade?

③ In a test the marks were 9, 3, 4, 7, 7. Calculate the mean mark.

④ For each set of numbers find **(i)** the mean **(ii)** the median
a) 8, 5, 9, 8, 7
b) 1, 5, 6, 11, 3, 4, 5
c) 4, 9, 2, 5.

⑤ The marks awarded to a skater were
58, 60, 57, 59, 56.
Find the mean mark.

⑥ The shoe sizes of the children in a Year 7 class were
3, 2, 3, 4, 3, 2, 3, 4, 3, 2, 3, 3
3, 3, 4, 5, 3, 4, 3, 3, 3, 5, 2, 3.
What shoe size is the mode?

⑦ The temperature in a garden was measured at midnight every day for a week. The
results (in °C) were
-3, 0, 1, 7, -5, 3, 0
What was the range of the temperatures?

E

(1) a) Calculate the mean of the numbers 3, 2, 5, 11, 9, 6.

b) Calculate the new mean when the highest number is removed.

(2) In a maths test the marks for the boys were 9, 3, 5, 7, 4, 8 and the marks for the girls were 12, 16, 6, 10.

a) Find the mean mark for the boys.

b) Find the mean mark for the girls.

c) Find the mean mark for the whole class.

(3) The number of computer games owned by 33 children in a class is as follows:

2 4 3 4 1 4 2 4 1 5 2
3 0 5 3 4 3 6 7 3 3 6
4 1 4 2 0 1 4 3 2 5 0

What is the modal number of computer games in this class (ie the mode)?

(4) The temperature was recorded at midnight in seven towns. The readings were

0°, 1°, −4°, 1°, −2°, −5°, −4°

What was the median temperature?

(5) Eleven children receive the following amounts of pocket money each week:

£2, £1, £2·50, 80p, £2·50, £3, £3·20, 50p, 75p, £1·50, £1·20

What is the median amount of pocket money?

(6) Find the mode for the following set of numbers:

5, 5, 6, 8, 9, 10, 10, 11

There are two modes. Write them both down.

(7) Seven people have the following heights (in cm):

160, 155, 161, 146, 152, 160, 149

What is the range of their heights?

(8) The goals scored by ten footballers in the Premiership in a season were:

17, 14, 15, 8, 10, 12, 18, 11, 6, 9

What is the mean number of goals scored?

(9) The range for nine numbers on a card is 60. One number is covered by a piece of blu-tac. What could that number be?

55	22	13
38	61	10
24	44	▓

(10) Think of five numbers which have a mean of 6 and a median of 4. Ask a friend to check your answer.

On these pages you will learn to draw and interpret bar charts and line graphs.

If the spread of a set of data is too large it is usually necessary to group the data before displaying it in the form of a graph.

Example
The ages of Mrs. Evans' family on the occasion of her 100th birthday party.

78	18	1	35	26	9
54	32	45	15	11	59
39	42	0	33	21	74
6	28	48	7	24	12
100	57	37	3	81	60

A tally chart showing the grouped ages.

Age	Tally	Frequency
0–19	ЖЖ ЖЖ	10
20–39	ЖЖ IIII	9
40–59	ЖЖ I	6
60–79	III	3
80–99	I	1
100+	I	1
Total		30

The data in the tally chart can be displayed in a graph.

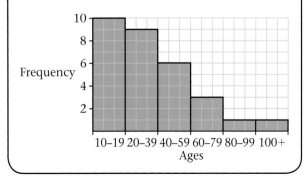

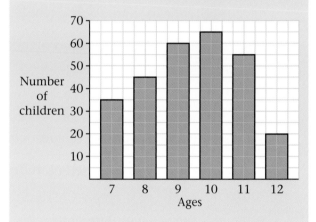

① This bar chart shows the ages of children at a school disco.

a) How many children were 9?

b) How many children were 11?

c) What was the age of the oldest child?

d) How many children were younger than 9?

e) How many children were older than 9?

f) How many children were there at the disco?

② The distances achieved in a Welly Throwing Competition in metres.

19 24 37 22 18 29 42 14 10 26
31 16 23 30 36 8 27 11 32 24

Group the data in 10 metre intervals [0–9, 10–19 etc]
Make a tally chart and then display the data in a bar chart.

The rupee is the currency used in India.
This graph converts rupees into pounds.

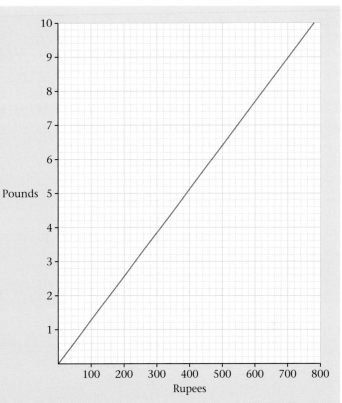

③ Convert into pounds:
   a) 280 rupees   d) 660 rupees
   b) 420 rupees   e) 380 rupees
   c) 600 rupees   f) 40 rupees.

④ Convert into rupees:
   a) £8·00   d) £7·40
   b) £4·60   e) £2·00
   c) £10·00   f) £6·60.

⑤ On holiday in India, Stanley bought snake charming lessons worth 9 pounds.
   How much did he pay in rupees?

⑥ This graph shows the distance children in Year 7 travel to school.

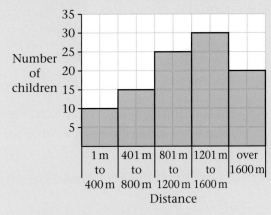

a) How many children live nearer to the School than 801 m?
b) How many children live further from the School than 800 m?
c) How many children are there in Year 7?

⑦ The children in one class took the following numbers of minutes to travel to school.

23 51   9 34 12 14 32 53 18 27
 7 29 17   3 43 36 11 25 42 15
24 46 10 16   9 13   8 22 31 14

Group the data in sets of 10 minutes. Make a tally chart and then display the data in a bar chart.

E

1 The weights of the children in one Year 7 class in kilograms.

46 38 44 41 47 52 40 44 57 36
43 31 54 42 38 51 42 61 34 48
44 35 46 59 41 49 51 39 45 48

Group the data in sets of 5 kg.
Make a tally chart and then display the data in a bar chart.

2 This bar chart shows the percentage marks achieved by children in a Test.

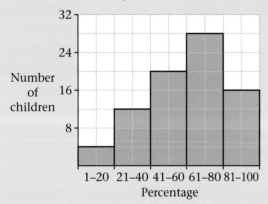

a) How many children scored below 41%?

b) How many children scored between 41% and 60%?

c) How many children scored more than 60%?

d) How many children took the test?

e) What proportion of the children scored over 80%?
Give your answer as a percentage.

3 This graph converts U.S. dollars to pounds.

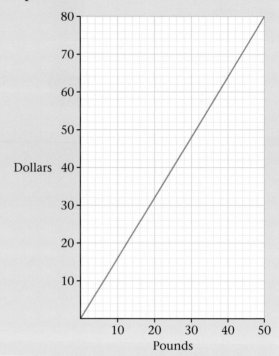

Convert into pounds:

a) 40 dollars   d) 16 dollars
b) 64 dollars   e) 48 dollars
c) 70 dollars   f) 24 dollars.

4 Convert into dollars:

a) £20   d) £36
b) £16   e) £6
c) £50   f) £34.

5 Before flying home from New York the Wilson family bought gifts for 72 dollars.
How much did they spend in pounds?

On these pages you will learn how to work out the chance of certain events happening.

For simple events, like throwing a dice or tossing a coin, we can work out the expected probability of an event occurring.

For a fair dice the *expected probability* of throwing a '3' is $\frac{1}{6}$.

For a normal coin the expected probability of tossing a 'head' is $\frac{1}{2}$

> Expected probability $= \dfrac{\text{the number of ways the event can happen}}{\text{the number of possible outcomes}}$

Random choice: If a card is chosen at random from a pack it means that every card has an equal chance of being chosen.

Nine identical discs numbered 1, 2, 3, 4, 5, 6, 7, 8, 9 are put into a bag. One disc is selected at random.

a) The probability of selecting a '4' $= \frac{1}{9}$
   This may be written p (selecting a '4') $= \frac{1}{9}$
b) p (selecting an odd number) $= \frac{5}{9}$
c) p (selecting a number greater than 5) $= \frac{4}{9}$

Ⓜ

① A bag contains a red ball, a blue ball and a yellow ball. One ball is chosen at random. Copy and complete these sentences.

a) The probability that the red ball is chosen is ... $\frac{\square}{3}$

b) The probability that the blue ball is chosen is ... $\frac{\square}{\square}$

c) The probability that the yellow ball is chosen is ... $\frac{\square}{\square}$

② One ball is chosen at random from a bag which contains a red ball, a blue ball, a yellow ball and a white ball. Write down the probability that the chosen ball will be

a) red   b) blue   c) yellow.

3 One ball is chosen at random from a box which contains 2 red balls and 2 blue balls. Write down the probability that the chosen ball will be
a) red
b) blue
c) yellow.

4 A hat contains 2 white balls and 1 black ball. One ball is chosen at random. Find the probability that it is
a) white   b) black.

5 A pencil case contains pencils of the following colours: 6 red, 3 black, 1 green and 1 blue. One pencil is selected without looking. Find the probability that the pencil is
a) red   b) black   c) green.

6 I roll an ordinary dice.
Find the probability that I score
a) 3
b) 1
c) less than 5.

7 Eight identical discs numbered 1, 2, 3, 4, 5, 6, 7, 8 are put into a bag. One disc is selected at random. Find the probability of selecting
a) a '5'.   b) an odd number.   c) a number less than 6.

8 Nine identical discs numbered 1, 3, 4, 5, 7, 8, 10, 11, 15 are put into a bag. One disc is selected at random. Find the probability of selecting.
a) a '10'.   b) an even number.   c) a number more than 6.

9 A bag contains 4 red balls and 7 white balls. One ball is selected at random. Find the probability that it is
a) red.   b) white.

10 One card is selected at random from the ten cards shown ...
Find the probability of selecting
a) the King of spades   b) a heart
c) a diamond   d) a 3

11 A bag contains 2 red balls, 4 white balls and 5 blue balls. One ball is selected at random. Find the probability of selecting.
a) a red ball   b) a white ball   c) a blue ball

12 I buy a fish at random from a pond containing 3 piranhas, 3 baby sharks and 7 goldfish. Find the probability that the fish I choose is
a) a goldfish   b) a baby shark
c) dangerous   d) glad I rescued it!
e) able to play the piano.

A pack of playing cards, without Jokers, contains 52 cards.

There are Ace, King, Queen, Jack, 10, 9, 8, 7, 6, 5, 4, 3, 2 of four suits.

The suits are …

spades   hearts   diamonds   clubs

A pack of cards is shuffled and then one card is chosen at random.

a) The probability that it is a King of hearts is $\frac{1}{52}$

b) The probability that it is an ace is $\frac{4}{52}$ $(= \frac{1}{13})$

c) The probability that it is a spade is $\frac{13}{52}$ $(= \frac{1}{4})$

E

(1) One card is picked at random from a pack of 52.

Find the probability that it is
a) a Queen   **b)** the King of diamonds   **c)** a spade

(2) One card is selected at random from a full pack of 52 playing cards. Find the probability of selecting
a) a heart   **b)** a red card   **c)** a '2'
d) any King, Queen or Jack   **e)** the ace of spades

(3) A small pack of twenty cards consists of the Ace, King, Queen, Jack and 10 of spades, hearts, diamonds and clubs. One card is selected at random. Find the probability of selecting
a) the ace of hearts   **b)** a King   **c)** a '10'
d) a black card   **e)** a heart

(4) A bag contains 3 black balls, 2 green balls, 1 white ball and 5 orange balls. Find the probability of selecting
a) a black ball   **b)** an orange ball   **c)** a white ball

(5) A bag contains the balls shown. One ball is taken out at random.
Find the probability that it is
a) yellow   **b)** blue   **c)** red

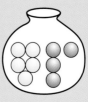

One more blue ball and one more red ball are added to the bag.

d) Find the new probability of selecting a yellow ball from the bag.

On these pages you will do some experiments to see if you can guess what will happen.

M

① Half the numbers on a dice are the odd numbers 1, 3 and 5.
If you roll a dice, the probability of getting an odd number is $\frac{1}{2}$.
Copy the table below and complete the second row.

Number of rolls of dice	10	20	30	40	50	60
Number of odd numbers we expect						
Number of odd numbers we actually got						

Roll a dice 60 times, filling in the last row of the table after every 10 rolls.
Discuss your answers with your teacher.

② If you roll a dice, the probability of getting a 2 is $\frac{1}{6}$.
Copy the table below and complete the second row.

Number of rolls of dice	12	24	36	48	60
Number of 2s we expect					
Number of 2s we actually got					

Roll a dice 60 times, filling in the last row every 12 rolls.
Discuss your answers with your teacher.

E

① If we toss a drawing pin, what is the probability that it will land 'point up'?
Copy this tally chart.

Number of throws	Number of times the pin lands 'point up'.

Toss a drawing pin 100 times, filling in your tally chart after each throw.

Example

Number of throws	Number of times the pin lands 'point up'
⊮⊮⊮ ⊮⊮⊮ ‖	⊮⊮⊮ ‖‖

When you have finished, you can work out the probability of the drawing pin landing 'point up' by the following rule:

$$\frac{\text{Number of times the pin lands 'point up'}}{100 \text{ throws}}$$

Work this out with a calculator and discuss with your teacher.

This answer might be different next time you do the experiment.

We call it an experimental probability.

② Make up your own experiment
using a pack of cards.
Think of an event like:
'drawing an ace'
'selecting a red card'
'drawing a picture card'

Make a tally chart as before
and find the experimental
probability of the event occurring.

This page will ask you to collect some data by designing a collection sheet, making a frequency table, drawing a chart and saying something about what you have found.

Task

How many hours of TV did children in my class watch last week?
(Your teacher should help you).

Get your teacher to help you design a data collection sheet

It might look like this:

Hours of TV	Tally
0–9	
10–19	
20–39	
40–59	
50–59	

When your teacher is happy with your chart, ask all the people in your class how many hours of TV they watched last week. Fill in your chart.

Add up your tally numbers to make and complete a frequency table.

It might look like this:

Hours of TV	Frequency
0–9	
10–19	
20–39	
40–59	
50–59	

You must now show this data on a bar chart.

It might look like this:
Write down which of *your* bars had the most children. (We call this the modal group).

Did you expect this?

If you had time, what else could you find out about TV and children?

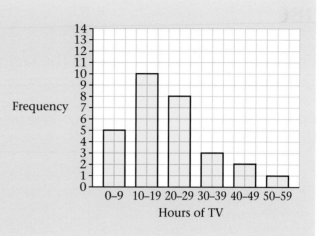

E

This needs a computer with a spreadsheet.
[Teachers' note: See answer book for help with using 'Excel'.]

Task 1
Do the 'hours of TV' survey on a spreadsheet.
You need to make and print a title, a frequency table and a bar chart with labels.
(You may need to do some spreadsheet work with your teacher first).
Finally, write on the modal group (or type it) and anything else you want to say.

Task 2
Can you use the spreadsheet to make and print out a pie chart instead of a bar chart?

Task 3
If you have time, find out how many dvds children in your class have.
Can you make and print a title, a frequency table and a bar chart with labels for this data?
Can you find the modal number of dvds?

On these pages you will find all the factors of numbers from 1 to 40.

> Remember: A factor is a number which divides exactly into another number (there will be no remainder).

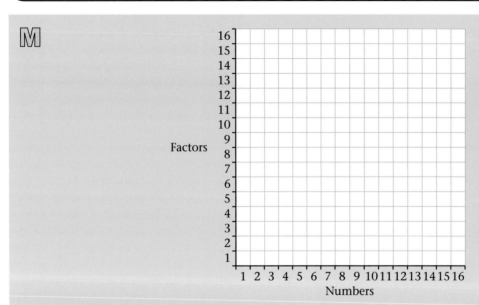

For each number 1 to 16 along the bottom, you must shade in the boxes above for any factor of that number.

Example

4 has factors 1, 2 and 4 so shade in those factor boxes above the number 4.

5 has factors 1 and 5 so shade in those factor boxes above the number 5.

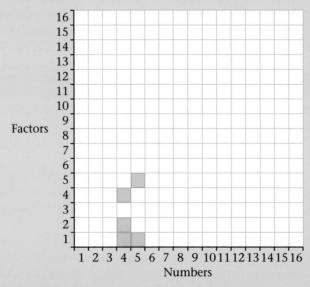

Complete your chart for all the numbers.

Count up how many boxes you have shaded and write down the answer.

E

Copy this onto square paper.

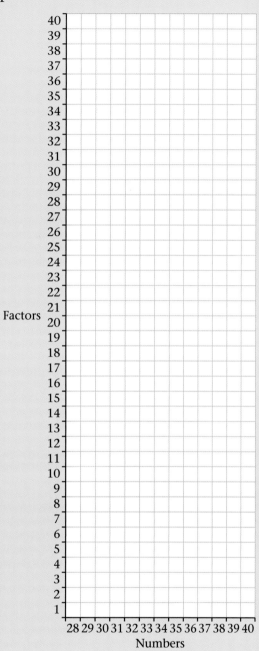

Factors

Numbers

Fill in the factor boxes above each number along the bottom. Count up how many boxes you have shaded and write down the answer.

On these pages you will practise the multiplication and division facts for
6, 7, 8, 9

Ⓜ **Part 1**

Write the answers only.

① 40 × 6
② 200 × 6
③ 500 × 6
④ 70 × 6
⑤ 30 × 6

⑥ 800 × 6
⑦ 400 × 6
⑧ 700 × 6
⑨ 90 × 6
⑩ 600 × 6

⑪ 120 ÷ 6
⑫ 600 ÷ 6
⑬ 240 ÷ 6
⑭ 6000 ÷ 6
⑮ 3600 ÷ 6

⑯ 300 ÷ 6
⑰ 4800 ÷ 6
⑱ 1800 ÷ 6
⑲ 420 ÷ 6
⑳ 5400 ÷ 6

Work out by multiplying by 6 and doubling.

㉑ 3 × 12
㉒ 10 × 12
㉓ 5 × 12
㉔ 2 × 12
㉕ 8 × 12

㉖ 6 × 12
㉗ 4 × 12
㉘ 9 × 12
㉙ 7 × 12
㉚ 20 × 12

㉛ There are six chairs in every stack.
There are 24 stacks. How many chairs
are there?

㉜ Eggs are packed into boxes of 6.
How many boxes are needed for
96 eggs?

Part 2

Write the answers only.

① 30 × 9
② 50 × 9
③ 70 × 9
④ 20 × 9
⑤ 300 × 9
⑥ 400 × 9
⑦ 80 × 9
⑧ 600 × 9
⑨ 500 × 9
⑩ 900 × 9

⑪ 270 ÷ 9
⑫ 450 ÷ 9
⑬ 180 ÷ 9
⑭ 810 ÷ 9
⑮ 360 ÷ 9
⑯ 5400 ÷ 9
⑰ 9000 ÷ 9
⑱ 720 ÷ 9
⑲ 1800 ÷ 9
⑳ 6300 ÷ 9

Work out by multiplying by 9 and
doubling.

㉑ 3 × 18
㉒ 6 × 18
㉓ 2 × 18
㉔ 30 × 18
㉕ 5 × 18

㉖ 8 × 18
㉗ 20 × 18
㉘ 4 × 18
㉙ 9 × 18
㉚ 7 × 18

㉛ A multi storey car park has 9 levels.
There are 36 parking spaces on each
level. How many cars can park in the
car park?

㉜ A school buys some tennis rackets for
£153. Each racket costs £9. How many
rackets does the school buy?

E **Part 1**

Write the answers only.

① 20 × 7   ⑪ 490 ÷ 7

② 50 × 7   ⑫ 280 ÷ 7

③ 80 × 7   ⑬ 140 ÷ 7

④ 400 × 7   ⑭ 5600 ÷ 7

⑤ 200 × 7   ⑮ 350 ÷ 7

⑥ 70 × 7   ⑯ 2100 ÷ 7

⑦ 300 × 7   ⑰ 420 ÷ 7

⑧ 90 × 7   ⑱ 630 ÷ 7

⑨ 600 × 7   ⑲ 7000 ÷ 7

⑩ 800 × 7   ⑳ 4900 ÷ 7

Work out by multiplying by 7 and doubling.

㉑ 5 × 14   ㉖ 8 × 14

㉒ 2 × 14   ㉗ 30 × 14

㉓ 6 × 14   ㉘ 4 × 14

㉔ 9 × 14   ㉙ 7 × 14

㉕ 3 × 14   ㉚ 60 × 14

㉛ How many weeks are there in 224 days?

㉜ Each minibus can carry 13 passengers. How many passengers can be carried in 7 minibuses?

㉝ What number is seven times greater than seven times seven?

Part 2

Write the answers only.

① 40 × 8   ⑪ 320 ÷ 8

② 20 × 8   ⑫ 160 ÷ 8

③ 700 × 8   ⑬ 4800 ÷ 8

④ 300 × 8   ⑭ 240 ÷ 8

⑤ 50 × 8   ⑮ 3200 ÷ 8

⑥ 200 × 8   ⑯ 640 ÷ 8

⑦ 90 × 8   ⑰ 800 ÷ 8

⑧ 500 × 8   ⑱ 5600 ÷ 8

⑨ 80 × 8   ⑲ 720 ÷ 8

⑩ 600 × 8   ⑳ 4000 ÷ 8

Work out by multiplying by 8 and doubling.

㉑ 2 × 16   ㉖ 6 × 16

㉒ 5 × 16   ㉗ 8 × 16

㉓ 7 × 16   ㉘ 4 × 16

㉔ 3 × 16   ㉙ 20 × 16

㉕ 9 × 16   ㉚ 30 × 16

㉛ There are eight cakes in each box. How many boxes are needed for 208 cakes?

㉜ A lorry travels the same route eight times every day. The route is 29 miles long. How far does the lorry travel in one day?

On this page you will learn to add or subtract 9, 19, 29 … or 11, 21, 31 …

Examples

$64 + 19 = 64 + 20 - 1$
$\quad\quad\quad = 84 - 1$
$\quad\quad\quad = 83$

$55 + 31 = 55 + 30 + 1$
$\quad\quad\quad = 85 + 1$
$\quad\quad\quad = 86$

$48 - 19 = 48 - 20 + 1$
$\quad\quad\quad = 28 + 1$
$\quad\quad\quad = 29$

M

Copy and complete the patterns.

(1) Add 9 ⟶ 7 ☐ ☐ 34

(2) Add 11 ⟶ 31 ☐ ☐ 64

(3) Add 19 ⟶ 8 ☐ ☐ 65

(4) Add 21 ⟶ 12 ☐ ☐ 75

(5) Take 9 ⟶ 51 ☐ ☐ 24

(6) Take 11 ⟶ 48 ☐ ☐ 15

(7) Take 19 ⟶ 96 ☐ ☐ 39

(8) Take 21 ⟶ 89 ☐ ☐ 26

(9) Add 31 ⟶ 2 ☐ ☐ 95

(10) Take 29 ⟶ 99 ☐ ☐ 12

Add 11	Add 29
(11) 121	(19) 37
(12) 304	(20) 54
(13) 265	(21) 23
(14) 547	(22) 69

Take 9	Take 21
(15) 380	(23) 72
(16) 167	(24) 45
(17) 431	(25) 26
(18) 275	(26) 58

(27) A hamster ate 38 grapes on Monday and 112 grapes on Tuesday. How many is that altogether?

E

Copy and complete.

(1) ☐ + 21 = 35

(2) ☐ + 41 = 98

(3) ☐ + 31 = 124

(4) ☐ + 61 = 149

(5) ☐ − 31 = 42

(6) ☐ − 61 = 27

(7) ☐ − 51 = 83

(8) ☐ − 81 = 76

(9) 21 + 37 = ☐

(10) 19 + ☐ = 50

Copy and complete the addition squares.

(11)

+	11	29	51	29
9				
30				
22				
31				

(12)

+	21	18	39	11
19				
41				
9				
20				

On this page you will learn to find a difference by counting up through the next multiple of 10, 100 or 1000

Examples

$33 - 25 = 5 + 3$
$\quad\quad\quad = 8$

$40 - 23 = 7 + 10$
$\quad\quad\quad = 17$

$300 - 287 = 3 + 10$
$\quad\quad\quad\quad = 13$

$94 - 47 = 3 + 40 + 4$
$\quad\quad\quad = 47$

$403 - 386 = 4 + 10 + 3$
$\quad\quad\quad\quad = 17$

$4003 - 3985 = 5 + 10 + 3$
$\quad\quad\quad\quad\quad = 18$

M

Work out

(1) $32 - 26$

(2) $51 - 47$

(3) $64 - 55$

(4) $85 - 78$

(5) $40 - 22$

(6) $50 - 27$

(7) $100 - 86$

(8) $200 - 192$

(9) $400 - 381$

(10) $103 - 90$

How many more must be added to these numbers to make:

(100)

(1000)

(11) 38

(12) 74

(13) 41

(14) 67

(15) 55

(16) 350

(17) 50

(18) 550

(19) 880

(20) 790

Work out

(21) $63 - 58$

(22) $300 - 188$

(23) $74 - 66$

(24) $5000 - 4992$

(25) $306 - 199$

(26) $705 - 495$

(27) $6000 - 5983$

(28) $2000 - 1942$

(29) $3002 - 2970$

(30) $107 - 88$

E

Find the output number

(1) $67 \longrightarrow \boxed{-29} \longrightarrow ?$

(2) $83 \longrightarrow \boxed{-35} \longrightarrow ?$

(3) $112 \longrightarrow \boxed{-95} \longrightarrow ?$

(4) $205 \longrightarrow \boxed{-187} \longrightarrow ?$

(5) $400 \longrightarrow \boxed{-180} \longrightarrow ?$

(6) $106 \longrightarrow \boxed{-78} \longrightarrow ?$

Copy and complete

(7) $604 - \square = 186$

(8) $703 - \square = 274$

(9) $6000 - \square = 3875$

(10) $512 - \square = 197$

(11) $915 - \square = 498$

(12) $6018 - \square = 3993$

(13) $9012 - \square = 4998$

(14) $9000 - \square = 5693$

(15) $7000 - \square = 3876$

(16) $3008 - \square = 1985$

On this page you will learn to partition and recombine.

Break 6, 7, 8, 9 into '5 and a bit'.

Example

$39 + 18 = (35 + 4) + (15 + 3)$
$\qquad\quad = (35 + 15) + (4 + 3)$
$\qquad\quad = 50 + 7 = 57$

Partition into 10s and units.

Example

$37 + 26 = (30 + 7) + (20 + 6)$
$\qquad\quad = (30 + 20) + (7 + 6)$
$\qquad\quad = 50 + 13 = 63$

M

Work out:

(1) 6 + 7
(2) 9 + 8
(3) 7 + 8
(4) 9 + 6
(5) 12 + 26
(6) 15 + 29
(7) 16 + 15
(8) 13 + 38

(9) 25 + 18
(10) 45 + 17
(11) 35 + 29
(12) 65 + 18
(13) 55 + 39
(14) 45 + 28
(15) 75 + 19
(16) 25 + 27

E

Work out by partitioning.

(1) 34 + 19
(2) 45 + 38
(3) 67 + 24
(4) 58 + 29
(5) 36 + 87
(6) 52 + 49
(7) 43 + 76
(8) 64 + 58

(9) 58 − 14
(10) 74 − 23
(11) 86 − 41
(12) 67 − 35
(13) 49 − 27
(14) 89 − 25
(15) 78 − 56
(16) 57 − 42

Now you will learn to add or subtract to the nearest multiple of 10 and adjust.

Examples

$46 + 29 = 46 + 30 - 1$
$\qquad\quad = 76 - 1$
$\qquad\quad = 75$

$94 - 29 = 94 - 30 + 1$
$\qquad\quad = 64 + 1$
$\qquad\quad = 65$

$85 - 31 = 85 - 30 - 1$
$\qquad\quad = 55 - 1$
$\qquad\quad = 54$

M

Work out:

(1) 62 + 9
(2) 48 − 19
(3) 36 + 21
(4) 69 − 31
(5) 54 + 19
(6) 65 − 19
(7) 63 + 31
(8) 84 − 21
(9) 48 + 19
(10) 56 − 19

(11) 73 + 29
(12) 67 − 19
(13) 97 + 48
(14) 85 − 29
(15) 48 + 31
(16) 93 − 51
(17) 74 + 62
(18) 176 − 61
(19) 68 + 39
(20) 154 − 49

E

Copy and complete

(1) ☐ + 68 = 324
(2) ☐ − 39 = 193
(3) ☐ + 52 = 817
(4) ☐ + 59 = 238
(5) ☐ − 99 = 369
(6) ☐ + 61 = 547
(7) ☐ + 72 = 263
(8) ☐ − 48 = 267
(9) ☐ + 96 = 514
(10) ☐ + 78 = 147

On this page you will look at some shape problems.

① Here is an L-shape:

Two L-shapes can be put together to make a bigger shape (they can only touch edge to edge).

Example

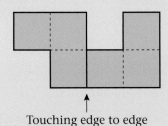

↑
Touching edge to edge

Draw shapes made from two L-shapes touching edge to edge where:

a) the new large shape has only one line of symmetry.

b) the new large shape has rotational symmetry of order 2.

c) make another large shape which only has one line of symmetry.

d) make another large shape which has rotational symmetry of order 2.

e) make a large shape with two lines of symmetry *and* rotational symmetry of order 2.

E

① You have 3 square green tiles and 2 square white tiles, which can be joined together along whole sides.

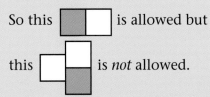

So this ▢▢ is allowed but

this ▢▢ is *not* allowed.

Draw as many diagrams as possible with the 5 tiles joined together so that the diagram has line symmetry.

For example fig. 1 and fig. 2 have line symmetry but fig. 3 does not have line symmetry so fig. 3 is not acceptable.

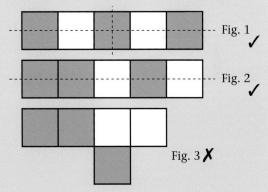

Fig. 1 ✓

Fig. 2 ✓

Fig. 3 ✗

② Now you have 2 black tiles and two white tiles. Draw as many diagrams as possible with these tiles joined together so that the diagram has line symmetry.

③ Finally with 3 black tiles and 3 white tiles draw as many diagrams as possible which have line symmetry.

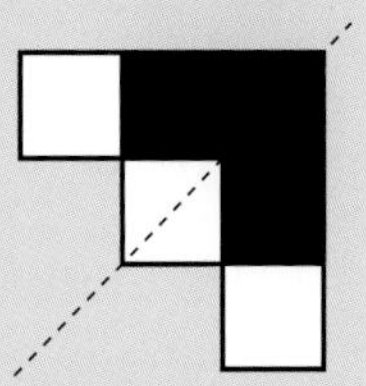

Here is one diagram which has line symmetry.

On these pages you will practise harder adding and subtracting.

Ⓜ **Part 1**

①	126 + 37	④	28 63 + 205	⑦	301 99 + 257	⑩	634 769 + 127
②	48 + 173	⑤	355 + 278	⑧	114 9 + 867	⑪	389 193 + 624
③	9 17 + 193	⑥	573 + 209	⑨	501 397 + 124	⑫	371 567 + 462

In Questions ⑬ to ㉜ set the problems out correctly in columns.

⑬ 3 + 12 + 109 　　　⑳ 679 + 63 + 4 　　　㉗ 8647 + 198

⑭ 27 + 260 　　　㉑ 54 + 507 + 2704 　　　㉘ 873 + 2316 + 473

⑮ 584 + 617 　　　㉒ 2030 + 69 + 5 　　　㉙ 2644 + 55 685

⑯ 39 + 357 　　　㉓ 6006 + 708 + 99 　　　㉚ 26 514 + 749

⑰ 3 + 109 + 61 　　　㉔ 842 + 67 + 2011 　　　㉛ 45 609 + 20 047

⑱ 5034 + 69 　　　㉕ 1089 + 891 + 19 + 9 　　　㉜ 26 514 + 749

⑲ 201 + 76 + 40 　　　㉖ 5867 + 321 + 45 + 9

Part 2

Copy each of the following problems and perform the calculation.

①	49 − 15	③	83 − 67	⑤	50 − 26	⑦	368 − 274	⑨	900 − 487
②	76 − 7	④	92 − 17	⑥	421 − 59	⑧	573 − 94	⑩	1001 − 697

In Questions ⑪ to ㉕ write the numbers in columns and then subtract.

⑪ 33 − 16 　　⑬ 57 − 19 　　⑮ 167 − 78 　　⑰ 743 − 517 　　⑲ 965 − 877

⑫ 24 − 7 　　⑭ 40 − 13 　　⑯ 319 − 234 　　⑱ 800 − 342 　　⑳ 2001 − 416

㉑ Two hundred and four take away forty-eight.

㉒ Five hundred and thirteen take away one hundred and twenty-five.

㉓ Two hundred and eight take away thirty one.

㉔ Six hundred and nineteen take away two hundred and twenty-seven.

㉕ Seven hundred and fifty take away three hundred and ninety-one.

E

Remember to line up the decimal points.

Copy and complete

1
$$4·12$$
$$-1·48$$

2
$$3·60$$
$$-1·26$$

3
$$2·94$$
$$-1·75$$

4
$$3·79$$
$$-2·4$$

5
$$4·68$$
$$-2·7$$

6
$$3·8$$
$$-2·79$$

7 In an egg and spoon race, a chicken weighed 3·1 kg and the egg weighed 0·26 kg.
Find the total weight.

Work out

8 46·3 − 17·5

9 23·2 + 8·6

10 2·36 + 1·57

11 4·6 + 1·19

12 2·3 − 2

13 5·17 + 2·4 + 3

14 7·1 + 8 + 2·13

15 6·14 + 3·6 + 2·41

16 A watch costs £13·50.
Find the change from £20.

17 £8·13 − £5·87

18 £4·62 − £3

19 £2·41 + £6 + £3·14

20 £5·21 + 83p + £2·64

21 Jemima has £7·63 in her purse. She spends £2·48. How much does she have left?

22 A sack of coal contains 46·4 kg. 8·5 kg is removed. How much coal is left?

Find the differences between

23 27·3 and 9·5

24 13·23 and 1·8

25 8·5 and 4·76

26 25·1 and 8·62

27 2·13 and 0·34

28 9·32 and 1·9

29 4·67 and 2

30 Rayan runs the 200 metres in 22·3 seconds. The winner runs 0·57 seconds faster. What is the winning time?

On this page you will practise multiplying.

Examples

Work from the right and carry.

$$
\begin{array}{r}
2\,7\,3 \\
\times \quad 8 \\
\hline
2\,1\,8\,4 \\
{\scriptstyle 5\;2}
\end{array}
\qquad
\begin{array}{r}
1\,2\,7\,4 \\
\times \quad 3 \\
\hline
3\,8\,2\,2 \\
{\scriptstyle 2\;1}
\end{array}
\qquad
\begin{array}{r}
4\cdot 3 \\
\times \quad 6 \\
\hline
2\,5\cdot 8 \\
{\scriptstyle 1}
\end{array}
\qquad
\begin{array}{r}
2\cdot 7 \\
\times \quad 4 \\
\hline
1\,0\cdot 8 \\
{\scriptstyle 2}
\end{array}
$$

M

1) $\begin{array}{r} 486 \\ \times \quad 3 \\ \hline \end{array}$

2) $\begin{array}{r} 573 \\ \times \quad 6 \\ \hline \end{array}$

3) $\begin{array}{r} 1847 \\ \times \quad 8 \\ \hline \end{array}$

4) $\begin{array}{r} 2792 \\ \times \quad 7 \\ \hline \end{array}$

5) $\begin{array}{r} 5483 \\ \times \quad 4 \\ \hline \end{array}$

6) $\begin{array}{r} 2875 \\ \times \quad 9 \\ \hline \end{array}$

Now do these.

7) 3936×7

8) 2648×9

9) 3759×8

10) 5273×4

11) 4349×6

12) 1963×9

13) A gambler lost £1218 on Friday and seven times as much next day. How much did he lose on Saturday?

E

1) $1\cdot6 \times 3$

2) $2\cdot4 \times 3$

3) $3\cdot1 \times 6$

4) $4\cdot2 \times 4$

5) $1\cdot8 \times 5$

6) $4\cdot3 \times 8$

7) $6\cdot7 \times 4$

8) $7\cdot8 \times 5$

9) $3\cdot4 \times 9$

10) $5\cdot8 \times 3$

11) $9\cdot6 \times 5$

12) $3\cdot5 \times 7$

13) One mile is about 1·6 kilometres. How far is 4 miles in kilometres?

14) A bucket holds 8·7 litres of water. How much water would 6 buckets hold?

15) A motorcyclist was in hospital for 87 hours in April. In May she stayed in hospital nine times as long. For how long was she in hospital in May?

16) A baby weighs 6·4 kilograms. His mother is nine times heavier. How much does his mother weigh?

On this page you will practise more long multiplication (2 digit by 2 digit numbers).

M

Work out

1. 32×57
2. 41×46
3. 63×28
4. 52×34
5. 58×69

6. 94×71
7. 83×46
8. 75×43
9. 53×88
10. 86×94

11. A saxaphone costs £83.

How much does a shop owner have to pay for 65 of these saxaphones?

E

1. Dean earns £28 each week from a part-time job. How much in total would he earn in 52 weeks?

2. 18 people each weigh 64kg. What is their total weight?

3. Jasmine receives £16 each week. How much money would she have received after 34 weeks?

4. A new computer game costs £39. How much would 45 computer games cost?

5. Ronaldo walks his dog 31 miles each week. How far does he walk his dog in 43 weeks?

6. Jason earns £76 each week. How much would he earn in total in 1 year (1 year is 52 weeks).

7. If a child uses 12 tubes of toothpaste each year, how many tubes of toothpaste would 86 children use in total each year?

8. A footballer is promised £75 for each goal he scores. How much money does he earn if he scores 27 goals.

9. A group of 14 friends go for a meal which costs £16 each. How much does the meal cost for all 14 friends?

10. A CD costs £16. How much will 24 CDs cost?

On these pages you will learn to make sensible decisions about rounding up or down after division.

- How many £6 tickets can I buy with £47?

  47 ÷ 6 = 7 remainder 5.
  Answer: 7 tickets can be bought.

- An egg box holds 6 eggs.
  How many boxes do I need to hold 47 eggs?

  47 ÷ 6 = 7 remainder 5.
  Answer: 8 boxes are needed.

- Each hospital ward holds fifteen patients.
  How many wards are needed for 70 patients?

  70 ÷ 15 = 4 remainder 10.
  Answer: 5 wards are needed.

- Each dress rail in a shop holds fifteen dresses.
  How many rails can be filled with 70 dresses?

  70 ÷ 15 = 4 remainder 10.
  Answer: 4 rails can be filled.

Ⓜ

① How many pairs of socks can be made from 27 socks?

② Darts are sold in packs of three. How many packs can be made from 20 darts?

③ 4 oranges can be packed into a bag. How many bags can be filled with 35 oranges?

④ Katie wants to buy a toy which costs £13. She saves £2 every week. How many weeks will it take her to save the £13 she needs?

⑤ 4 children can sit at a table. How many tables are needed to seat the 30 children in a class?

⑥ Pencils cost 10p. How many can be bought for £1·38?

⑦ Sharpeners are sold in packets of 6. How many packets does a school need to buy for a class of 32 children?

⑧ A car can carry 5 passengers. How many cars are needed to carry 42 passengers?

(9) A van can carry 8 large boxes. How many vans are needed to carry 50 boxes?

(10) How many 5-a-side football teams can be made up from 59 players?

(11) 6 children can sleep in a large tent. How many tents are needed for 75 children?

(12) Chocko chocolate bars are sold in packs of 6. How many packs can be made from 52 bars?

(13) 10 dvds can be stored on a shelf. How many shelves are needed to store 95 dvds?

(14) Tickets for a film show cost £3. How many tickets can be bought for £35?

E

(1) Tennis balls are sold in tubes. There are 4 balls in each tube. How many tubes can be filled from 70 balls?

(2) Craig saves £3 every week. How many weeks will it take him to save £20?

(3) How many complete weeks are there in 40 days?

(4) Each container holds nine litres of petrol. How many containers are needed for 50 litres?

(5) Cans of drink are sold in packs of 6. How many packs can be made from 94 cans?

(6) Each tray holds sixteen flowers. How many trays are needed for 120 flowers?

(7) A coach can carry 35 passengers. How many coaches are needed to carry 150 passengers?

(8) A baker puts his cakes onto trays which hold 8 cakes. How many trays are needed for 100 cakes?

(9) How many complete years are there in 70 months?

(10) Albert saved £600 every month.

How many months did it take him to save the £5000 he needed for his new car?

On this page you will practise dividing.

Examples:

$$4\overline{)5^13} \quad \begin{array}{r} 1\ 3\ r\ 1 \end{array}$$

$$7\overline{)5\ 2^33} \quad \begin{array}{r} 7\ 4\ r\ 5 \end{array}$$

$$2\overline{)8\cdot2\ 6} \quad \begin{array}{r} 4\cdot1\ 3 \end{array}$$

$$3\overline{)4\ \cdot^11^21} \quad \begin{array}{r} 1\ \cdot\ 3\ 7 \end{array}$$

M

(1) $138 \div 6$

(2) $314 \div 7$

(3) $250 \div 8$

(4) $423 \div 9$

(5) $347 \div 6$

(6) $183 \div 7$

(7) $224 \div 8$

(8) $687 \div 9$

(9) $201 \div 6$

(10) $369 \div 7$

(11) $377 \div 8$

(12) $348 \div 9$

(13) $290 \div 6$

(14) $272 \div 7$

(15) $530 \div 8$

(16) $833 \div 9$

(7) There were 245 passengers on a plane. One seventh of the passengers got off at Paris. How many flew on to New York?

(18) Eight magazines weigh 536 grams. How much does one weigh?

E

Work out and give the remainder as a whole number.

(1) $63 \div 4$

(2) $51 \div 7$

(3) $67 \div 9$

(4) $44 \div 6$

(5) $121 \div 5$

(6) $128 \div 10$

(7) $72 \div 5$

(8) $278 \div 9$

(9) $53 \div 8$

(10) $226 \div 100$

Work out

(11) $4\cdot2 \div 3$

(12) $8\cdot5 \div 5$

(13) $8\cdot52 \div 4$

(14) $7\cdot10 \div 5$

(15) $8\cdot52 \div 6$

(16) £7·30 ÷ 2

(17) £6·00 ÷ 5

(18) £7·40 ÷ 4

(19) £8·50 ÷ 5

(20) £14·00 ÷ 8

(21) A box of 4 CDs costs £15·00. What is the cost of each CD?

(22) Eight friends share the cost of a meal. The bill comes to £36·00. How much should each person pay?

(23) Five train tickets cost £19·00. What does one ticket cost?

On this page you will learn to use the brackets and square root keys on a calculator.

Examples:

$(8.35 - 1.2) \times 1.6$

Press $\boxed{(}$ $\boxed{8.35}$ $\boxed{-}$ $\boxed{1.2}$ $\boxed{)}$ $\boxed{\times}$ $\boxed{1.6}$ $\boxed{=}$

Answer = 11.44

$\sqrt{3600} \times \sqrt{81}$

$\boxed{\sqrt{\;}}$ $\boxed{3600}$ $\boxed{\times}$ $\boxed{\sqrt{\;}}$ $\boxed{81}$ $\boxed{=}$

Answer = 540

Ⓜ

Use a calculator to work out the problems and interpret the display.

1. $6.2 - 2.7$

2. $8.3 - 3.6$

3. $7.54 - 1.2$

4. $14.5 - 5.93$

5. $63.14 - 9.75$

6. $11.4 - 5.32$

7. $(£2.76 + 69p) \times 8$

8. $(£6.35 - 87p) \times 5$

9. $(£4.36 - 68p) \times 15$

10. $(£3.12 - 57p) \times 4$

11. $(£36.44 + 76p) \div 8$

12. $(£77.83 + 57p) \div 16$

13. $(92 - 65) \times (46 + 87)$

14. $(66 + 49) \times (63 - 27)$

15. $(84 - 38) \times (47 + 29)$

16. $(173 - 128) \times (94 - 67)$

17. $(64 - 38) \times (4.7 + 2.9)$

18. $(5.4 - 2.9) \times (68 + 47)$

Ⓔ

Remember $\sqrt{16} = 4$ because $4 \times 4 = 16$
We say the *square root* of 16 is 4.
Work out

1. $\sqrt{81}$

2. $\sqrt{144}$

3. $\sqrt{169}$

4. $\sqrt{225}$

5. $\sqrt{2.56}$

6. $\sqrt{12.96}$

7. $\sqrt{20.25}$

8. $\sqrt{16} - \sqrt{9}$

9. $\sqrt{144} - \sqrt{64}$

10. $\sqrt{625} - \sqrt{361}$

11. $\sqrt{256} + \sqrt{36}$

12. $\sqrt{576} + \sqrt{25}$

13. $\sqrt{1296} + \sqrt{441}$

14. $\sqrt{400} - \sqrt{100}$

15. $\sqrt{324} - \sqrt{49}$

16. $3 \times \sqrt{121}$

17. $4 \times \sqrt{49}$

18. $5 \times \sqrt{169}$

19. $8 \times \sqrt{81}$

20. $\sqrt{36} \times \sqrt{144}$

21. $\sqrt{225} \div \sqrt{25}$

22. $\sqrt{1024} \div \sqrt{64}$

23. $\sqrt{2500} \div \sqrt{100}$

24. $(\sqrt{196} - \sqrt{16}) \times 4$

25. $(\sqrt{225} + \sqrt{1521}) \times 3$

26. $(\sqrt{576} - \sqrt{289}) \times 10$

27. $(\sqrt{121} - \sqrt{9}) \times (\sqrt{169} + \sqrt{4})$

28. Find a number which multiplies by itself to give 729.

29. Find a number which multiplies by itself to give 2116.

30. How long is one side of a square if the area is 324 cm²?

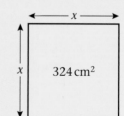

(1) Hannah has the following coins:

   a) Which coin is the **mode**?

   b) What is the **range** of the value of these coins?

(2) This graph converts American dollars
into pounds.

   a) Convert 6 dollars into pounds.

   b) Omar changed £10 into dollars.
How many dollars did he get?

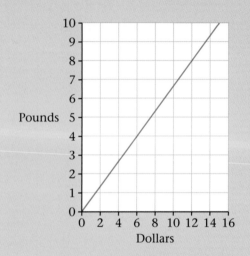

(3) 6 children had the following pocket money each month:

     £10   £20   £8   £8   £25   £19

Find the **mean** amount of pocket money.

(4) Year 7 are asked what their favourite
pets are:
These are the results.

   a) How many children like dogs and
rabbits in total?

   b) How **many more** children liked
cats than hamsters?

   c) How many children were asked
about their favourite pets?

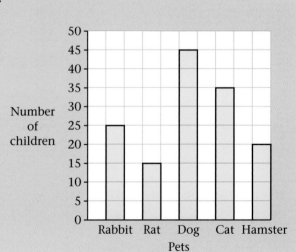

⑤ Work out 2065 + 387 + 64 + 3

⑥ Write down the number in the empty box.

$$\boxed{} \times 7 = 56$$

⑦ Danny is 1·63 m tall.
Silvio is 1·47 m tall.
How much taller is Danny than Silvio?
Give your answer in centimetres.

⑧ 32 crayons are shared equally between 8 children.
How many crayons does each child get?

⑨ List all the factors of 28.

⑩ Write down the order of rotational symmetry of this shape.

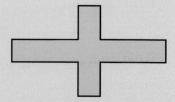

Ask for tracing paper if it will help.

⑪ Copy the shape below on squared paper.

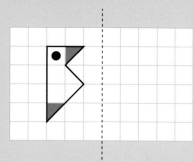

Draw the dotted line.
Draw the reflection of the shape in the dotted line.
You may use a mirror or tracing paper.

⑫ Work out 274 × 53

⑬ 46 people each saved £29. How much money did they save in total?

⑭ Copy and write in the missing digits to make this correct.

$$\begin{array}{r} \boxed{}\,3\,\boxed{} \\ \times\quad 8 \\ \hline 1\ 8\ 5\ 6 \end{array}$$

⑮

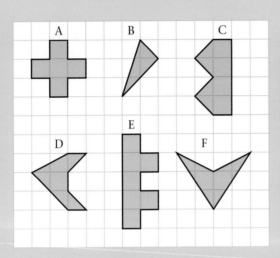

Which **four** shapes above have **reflective symmetry**?
You may use a mirror or tracing paper.

⑯ Work out 4·2 × 4

⑰ 3 children go to the cinema and each pay £3·65.
How much money in total does it cost the 3 children to go to the cinema?

⑱ A bag contains 2 red balls, 3 blue balls and 1 yellow ball. One ball is chosen at random.

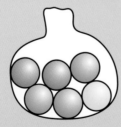

a) What is the probability that the yellow ball is chosen?
b) What is the probability that a blue ball is chosen?

(19) Copy the shape below on squared paper.

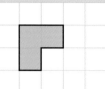

Translate the shaded shape **right 3 squares** and **down 2 squares**.
Draw the new shape.

(20)

I roll an ordinary dice.
What is the probability that I score
a) 4
b) less than 4?

On these pages you will solve crossnumber puzzles.

Here are cross number puzzles with a difference. There are no clues, only answers, and you have to find where the answers go.

a) Copy out the cross number pattern.

b) Fit all the given numbers into the correct spaces. Work logically and tick off the numbers from lists as you write them in the squares.

1. Ask your teacher if you do not know how to start.

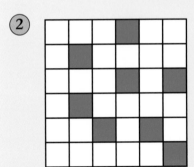

2 digits	3 digits	4 digits	5 digits	6 digits
18	375	1274	37125	308 513
37	692	1625		
53	828	3742		
74		5181		
87				

2.

2 digits	3 digits	4 digits	5 digits	6 digits
13	382	2630	12 785	375 041
21	582	2725		
45	178	5104		
47		7963		
72				

3.

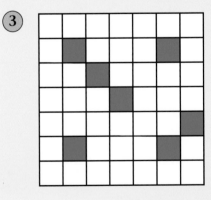

2 digits	3 digits	4 digits	6 digits
53	182	4483	375 615
63	324	4488	
64	327	6515	*7 digits*
	337		3 745 124
	436		4 253 464
	573		8 253 364
	683		8 764 364
	875		

④

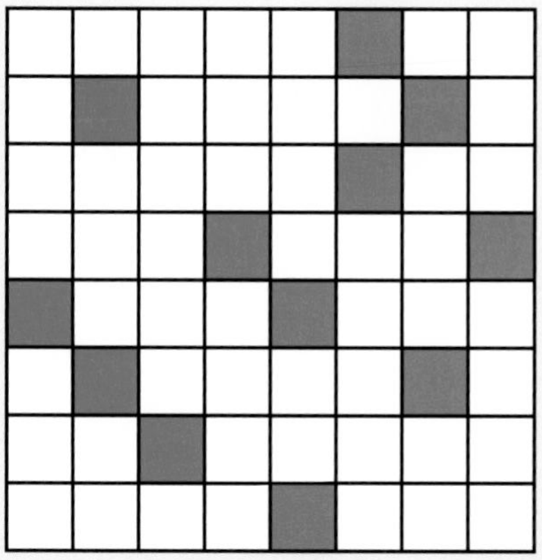

2 digits	3 digits	4 digits	5 digits	6 digits
27	161	1127	34 462	455 185
36	285	2024	74 562	
54	297	3473	81 072	
63	311	5304	84 762	
64	412	5360		
69	483	5370		
	535	5380		
	536			
	636			
	714			

⑤

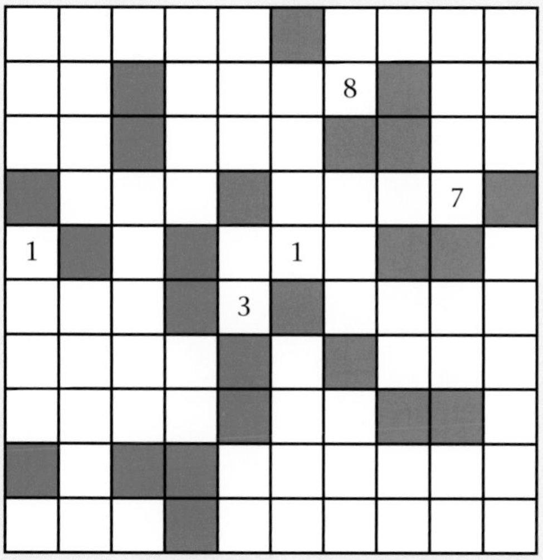

2 digits	3 digits	4 digits	5 digits	6 digits
21	121	1349	24 561	215 613
22	136	2457	24 681	246 391
22	146	2458	34 581	246 813
23	165	3864		
36	216	4351		
53	217	4462		
55	285	5321		
56	335	5351		
58	473	5557		
61	563	8241		
82	917	8251		
83		9512		
91				

Decimals, Fractions and Percentages 2

On these pages you will again use decimals, fractions and percentages.

> **Remember:**
>
> 42% means $\frac{42}{100}$
>
> and $\frac{42}{100}$ means 0·42
>
> so 42% = $\frac{42}{100}$ = 0·42

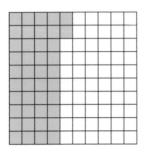

Ⓜ

Change these percentages into fractions:

① 2%
② 11%

③ 48%
④ 40%

⑤ 33%
⑥ 25%

Change these fractions into percentages:

⑦ $\frac{3}{10}$
⑧ $\frac{64}{100}$

⑨ $\frac{17}{100}$
⑩ $\frac{1}{4}$

⑪ $\frac{6}{10}$
⑫ $\frac{9}{10}$

Change these decimals into fractions:

⑬ 0·3
⑭ 0·2

⑮ 0·09
⑯ 0·58

⑰ 0·7
⑱ 0·07

Change these percentages into decimals:

⑲ 5%
⑳ 4%

㉑ 23%
㉒ 60%

㉓ 39%
㉔ 30%

Change these decimals into percentages:

㉕ 0·02
㉖ 0·51

㉗ 0·76
㉘ 0·2

㉙ 0·5
㉚ 0·91

Change these fractions into decimals:

㉛ $\frac{3}{10}$
㉜ $\frac{8}{10}$

㉝ $\frac{7}{100}$
㉞ $\frac{48}{100}$

㉟ $\frac{54}{100}$
㊱ $\frac{3}{4}$

Remember: 10% of 90 means $\frac{1}{10}$ of 90 = 9

30% of 90 means 3 × (10% of 90)
= 3 × 9
= 27

Find:

(1) 10% of 30

(2) 20% of 30

(3) 70% of 30

(4) 10% of 50

(5) 40% of 50

(6) 30% of 20

(7) 80% of 70

(8) 25% of 28

(9) 90% of 80

(10) 25% of 52

For questions **(11)** to **(15)** below, answer the following:

a) How much is the price reduced by?

b) What is the sale price?

(11)
Bike £300
SALE
10% off

(13)
DVD Player £120
SALE
25% off

(15)
TV £500
SALE
30% off

(12)
Bag £30
SALE
30% off

(14)
Game £40
SALE
60% discount

For questions **(16)** to **(20)** below, write down which amount is the larger in each question:

(16) 20% of £40   or   10% of £90

(17) 25% of £60   or   20% of £80

(18) 40% of £90   or   5% of £800

(19) 10% of £200   or   30% of £60

(20) 5% of £320   or   25% of £64

On these pages you will use + − × ÷.

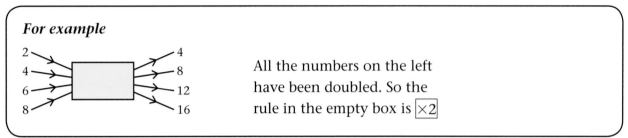

For example

All the numbers on the left have been doubled. So the rule in the empty box is $\boxed{\times 2}$

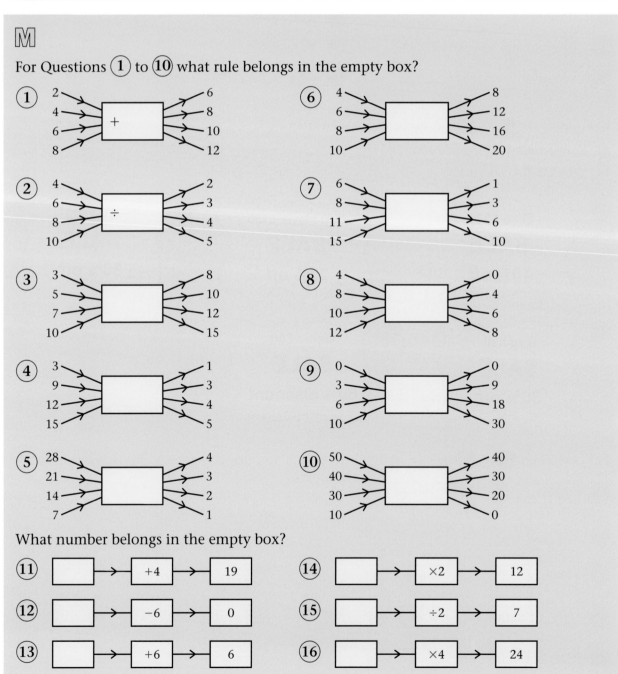

Ⓜ

For Questions ① to ⑩ what rule belongs in the empty box?

What number belongs in the empty box?

For Questions ① to ⑩ what rule belongs in the empty box?

①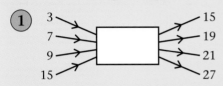

3 → 15
7 → 19
9 → 21
15 → 27

⑥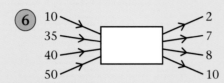

10 → 2
35 → 7
40 → 8
50 → 10

②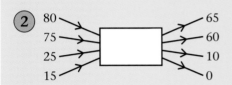

80 → 65
75 → 60
25 → 10
15 → 0

⑦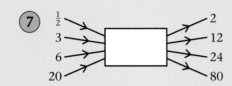

½ → 2
3 → 12
6 → 24
20 → 80

③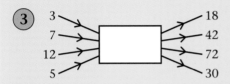

3 → 18
7 → 42
12 → 72
5 → 30

⑧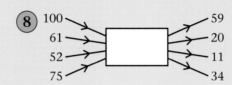

100 → 59
61 → 20
52 → 11
75 → 34

④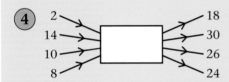

2 → 18
14 → 30
10 → 26
8 → 24

⑨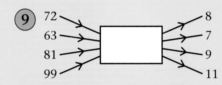

72 → 8
63 → 7
81 → 9
99 → 11

⑤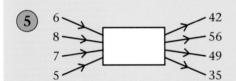

6 → 42
8 → 56
7 → 49
5 → 35

⑩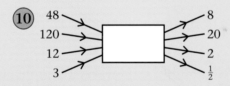

48 → 8
120 → 20
12 → 2
3 → ½

What number belongs in each empty box?

⑪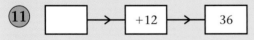

☐ → +12 → 36

⑫

☐ → ÷4 → 80

⑬

☐ → ×7 → 147

⑭

☐ → −16 → 27

⑮

☐ → ×9 → 108

⑯

☐ → ÷8 → 14

On these pages you will learn how to make an equation by using letters and numbers. You will also practise finding the value of the letter in an equation.

Example 1

Annie is thinking of a number.

If I add 3 to the number, the answer is 7

We could write $\boxed{n}$ for the mystery number.

So Annie said

$$\boxed{n} + 3 = 7$$

This is an equation. An equation has an '=' sign.

Example 2

Annie thinks of a number, subtracts 2 and the answer is 4.

Write this down as an equation using *n* for the mystery number.

Answer $n - 2 = 4$

For each question, write down an equation using *n* for the mystery number.

1. **a)** Annie thinks of a number, adds 2 and the answer is 6
   b) Annie thinks of a number, adds 5 and the answer is 7
   c) Annie thinks of a number, adds 4 and the answer is 8
   d) Annie thinks of a number, adds 6 and the answer is 9
   e) Annie thinks of a number, adds 5 and the answer is 11

   f) Annie thinks of a number, adds 4 and the answer is 7
   g) Annie thinks of a number, adds 8 and the answer is 10
   h) Annie thinks of a number, adds 2 and the answer is 9
   i) Annie thinks of a number, adds 3 and the answer is 9
   j) Annie thinks of a number, adds 7 and the answer is 10.

② For each equation in question ①, find the value of Annie's number.

③ For each question below write down an equation using *n* for the mystery number.
   a) Annie thinks of a number, subtracts 6 and the answer is 2
   b) Annie thinks of a number, subtracts 5 and the answer is 1
   c) Annie thinks of a number, subtracts 4 and the answer is 2
   d) Annie thinks of a number, subtracts 4 and the answer is 5
   e) Annie thinks of a number, subtracts 2 and the answer is 2

   f) Annie thinks of a number, subtracts 10 and the answer is 1
   g) Annie thinks of a number, subtracts 6 and the answer is 5
   h) Annie thinks of a number, subtracts 3 and the answer is 0
   i) Annie thinks of a number, subtracts 4 and the answer is 6
   j) Annie thinks of a number, subtracts 5 and the answer is 5.

④ For each equation in question ③, find the value of Annie's number.

Annie thinks of some trickier questions.

Example

Annie thinks of a number, multiplies it by 2, adds 3 and the answer is 7.

Write this down as an equation using *n* for the mystery number.

Answer

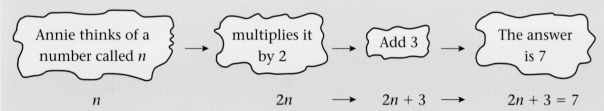

The equation is $2n + 3 = 7$.

① For each question, write down an equation using *n* for the mystery number.
   a) Annie thinks of a number, multiplies it by 2, adds 3 and the answer is 13
   b) Annie thinks of a number, multiplies it by 2, adds 4 and the answer is 8
   c) Annie thinks of a number, multiplies it by 3, adds 1 and the answer is 10
   d) Annie thinks of a number, multiplies it by 3, adds 4 and the answer is 10
   e) Annie thinks of a number, multiplies it by 4, adds 1 and the answer is 9

   f) Annie thinks of a number, multiplies it by 2, adds 1 and the answer is 9
   g) Annie thinks of a number, multiplies it by 3, adds 2 and the answer is 7
   h) Annie thinks of a number, multiplies it by 2, adds 4 and the answer is 4
   i) Annie thinks of a number, multiplies it by 3, adds 3 and the answer is 12
   j) Annie thinks of a number, multiplies it by 4, adds 3 and the answer is 1.

(2) How can we find the value of n if $2n + 3 = 7$?

Answer: $\boxed{2n} + 3 = 7$

↑

This box = 4 because $\boxed{4} + 3 = 7$

so $\boxed{2n} = 4$

↓

$2n$ means $2 \times n$.

so $2 \times n = 4$

so $n = 2$ because $2 \times \boxed{2} = 4$.

The mystery number is 2.

In the following questions, copy and fill the empty boxes.

a) $\boxed{2n} + 1 = 11$

  $\boxed{2n} = 10$

  $n = \boxed{}$

d) $\boxed{3n} + 1 = 10$

  $\boxed{3n} = \boxed{}$

  $n = \boxed{}$

g) $\boxed{4n} + 3 = 11$

  $\boxed{4n} = \boxed{}$

  $n = \boxed{}$

b) $\boxed{2n} + 5 = 15$

  $\boxed{2n} = \boxed{}$

  $n = \boxed{}$

e) $\boxed{2n} + 6 = 14$

  $\boxed{2n} = \boxed{}$

  $n = \boxed{}$

h) $\boxed{3n} + 2 = 11$

  $\boxed{3n} = \boxed{}$

  $n = \boxed{}$

c) $\boxed{2n} + 2 = 8$

  $\boxed{2n} = \boxed{}$

  $n = \boxed{}$

f) $\boxed{5n} + 1 = 11$

  $\boxed{5n} = 10$

  $n = \boxed{}$

i) $\boxed{5n} + 3 = 8$

  $\boxed{5n} = \boxed{}$

  $n = \boxed{}$

(3) Find the value of n in each of the following equations. (We call this *solving* the equation).

a) $2n + 1 = 5$

b) $3n + 1 = 7$

c) $3n + 2 = 14$

d) $4n + 1 = 9$

e) $4n - 1 = 11$

f) $5n - 2 = 13$

g) $2n - 5 = 15$

h) $3n + 2 = 17$

i) $2n + 7 = 9$

j) $5n - 2 = 18$

On these pages you will practise balancing both sides of an equation.

- Equations are like weighing scales which are balanced. The scales remain balanced if the same weight is added or taken away from both sides.

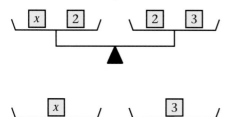

On the left pan is an unknown weight x plus a 2 kg weight.

On the right pan there is a 2 kg weight and a 3 kg weight.

If the two 2 kg weights are taken from each pan, the scales are *still balanced*.

So the weight x is 3 kg.

- Consider

Take off 2 from each pan.

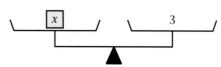

so $x = 3$.

- Consider

$x + 2 = 5$

Take off 2 from each side of the '=' sign.

$x = 3$

Ⓜ

In the following, find the value of x.

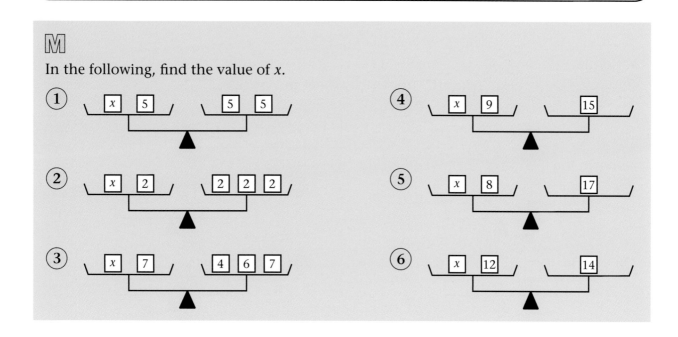

216

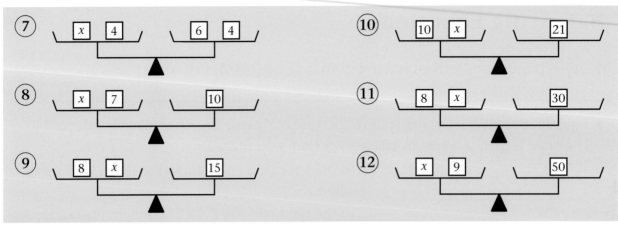

⑦ x 4 | 6 4

⑧ x 7 | 10

⑨ 8 x | 15

⑩ 10 x | 21

⑪ 8 x | 30

⑫ x 9 | 50

E

● Consider

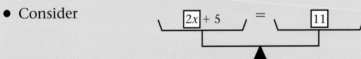

x x 5 | 11

Take off 5 from each pan.

x x | 6

Each $\boxed{x}$ must equal 3 because 2 $\boxed{x}$ boxes are equal to 6.
So $x = 3$.

● Consider

$\boxed{2x} + 5$ = $\boxed{11}$

Take off 5 from each pan.

$\boxed{2x}$ | $\boxed{6}$

So $x = 3$.

● Consider

$$2x + 5 = 11$$

Take off 5 from each side of the '=' sign

$$2x = 6$$

So $x = 3$ because $2 \times \boxed{x} = 6$.

Find x in the following.

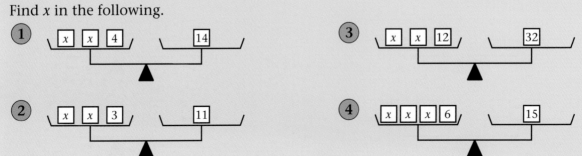

① x x 4 | 14

② x x 3 | 11

③ x x 12 | 32

④ x x x 6 | 15

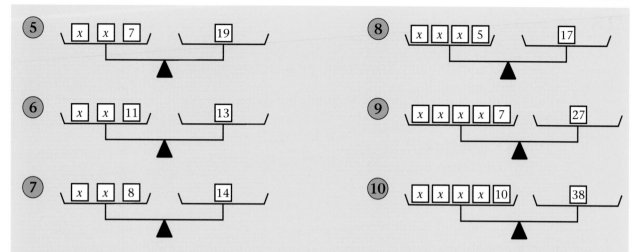

Use the balancing method to find x in each of the following questions.

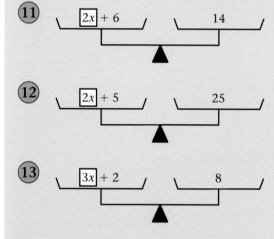

(14) $2x+9 = 19$

(15) $3x + 6 = 18$

(16) $2x + 10 = 24$

(17) $4x + 1 = 21$

(18) $4x + 6 = 18$

(19) $6x + 5 = 41$

(20) $5x + 9 = 44$

On these pages you will learn how to put numbers in place of letters.

> Remember: $3a$ means '$3 \times a$'
> $6a + 2$ means '$6 \times a$ then add 2'
> $2(a + 5)$ means '$a + 5$ then multiply by 2'
>
> **Examples**
> Find the value of each expression when $a = 2$.
> 1. $a + 3 = 2 + 3 = 5$
> 2. $4a = 4 \times 2 = 8$
> 3. $4a + 3 = 4 \times 2 + 3 = 11$
> 4. $4(a + 3) = 4 \times 5 = 20$
>
> Remember BODMAS. The order of operations is Brackets then $\div \times + -$.

Ⓜ

Find the value of each expression when $a = 3$.

① $a + 2$ ⑥ $2a$ ⑪ $2a + 3$ ⑯ $3(a + 1)$

② $a + 5$ ⑦ $3a$ ⑫ $3a + 1$ ⑰ $4(a + 2)$

③ $a + 6$ ⑧ $5a$ ⑬ $2a - 1$ ⑱ $5(a - 1)$

④ $a + 8$ ⑨ $7a$ ⑭ $4a - 2$ ⑲ $2(a + 4)$

⑤ $a + 4$ ⑩ $4a$ ⑮ $5a + 2$ ⑳ $4(a - 2)$

Find the value of each expression when $a = 2$ and $b = 3$.

㉑ $a + b$ ㉖ $2b + 3$ ㉛ $a + b + 6$ ㊱ $3a - 2b$

㉒ $2a + b$ ㉗ $3(a + 4)$ ㉜ $3a - b$ ㊲ $3(a + b + 2)$

㉓ $a + 2b$ ㉘ $4(b + 2)$ ㉝ $(a + b) \div 5$ ㊳ $4(a + b - 1)$

㉔ $2(a + b)$ ㉙ $a + 2b + 1$ ㉞ $2a + 2b$ ㊴ $(3a + b) \div 3$

㉕ $3a + 4$ ㉚ $2a + 3$ ㉟ $3a + 2b + 6$ ㊵ $2b - a$

E

Find the value of each expression when $b = 4$.

1 $b + 5$ **6** $2(b + 2)$ **11** $b \div 2 + 3$ **16** $2(b + 4)$

2 $b - 1$ **7** $3(b - 1)$ **12** $(b + 2) \div 3$ **17** $b + b$

3 $2b + 1$ **8** $5(b + 2)$ **13** $(b + 6) \div 5$ **18** $b + 10 + b$

4 $3b - 2$ **9** $4(b + 1)$ **14** $5(b - 2)$ **19** $b \times b$

5 $4b + 2$ **10** $6b - 10$ **15** $10b - 10$ **20** $100b$

Find the area of the following rectangles if $a = 2$ cm

$b = 4$ cm

$c = 3$ cm

Remember to give your answers in cm^2

21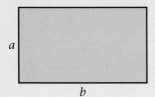
a b

25
c $a - 1$

29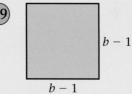
$b - 1$ $b - 1$

22
a a

26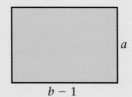
a $b - 1$

30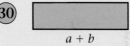
c $a + b$

23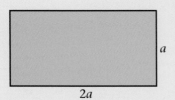
a $2a$

27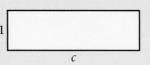
$b - 1$ c

31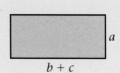
a $b + c$

24
c b

28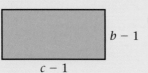
$b - 1$ $c - 1$

32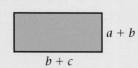
$a + b$ $b + c$

On these pages you will find rules which fit patterns of numbers.

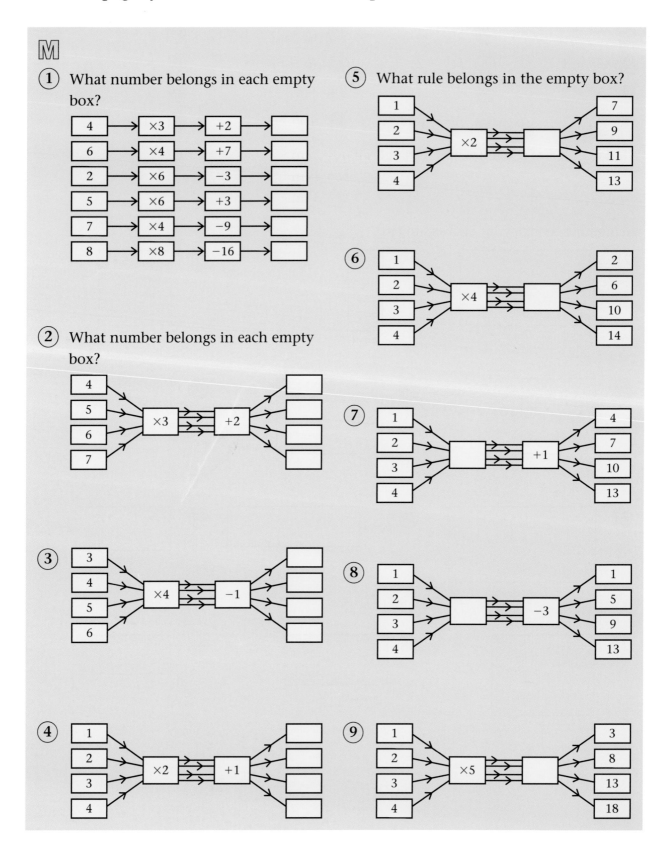

M

1. What number belongs in each empty box?

   4 → ×3 → +2 → ☐
   6 → ×4 → +7 → ☐
   2 → ×6 → −3 → ☐
   5 → ×6 → +3 → ☐
   7 → ×4 → −9 → ☐
   8 → ×8 → −16 → ☐

2. What number belongs in each empty box?

   4, 5, 6, 7 → ×3 → +2 → ☐ ☐ ☐ ☐

3. 3, 4, 5, 6 → ×4 → −1 → ☐ ☐ ☐ ☐

4. 1, 2, 3, 4 → ×2 → +1 → ☐ ☐ ☐ ☐

5. What rule belongs in the empty box?

   1, 2, 3, 4 → ×2 → ☐ → 7, 9, 11, 13

6. 1, 2, 3, 4 → ×4 → ☐ → 2, 6, 10, 14

7. 1, 2, 3, 4 → ☐ → +1 → 4, 7, 10, 13

8. 1, 2, 3, 4 → ☐ → −3 → 1, 5, 9, 13

9. 1, 2, 3, 4 → ×5 → ☐ → 3, 8, 13, 18

221

Example

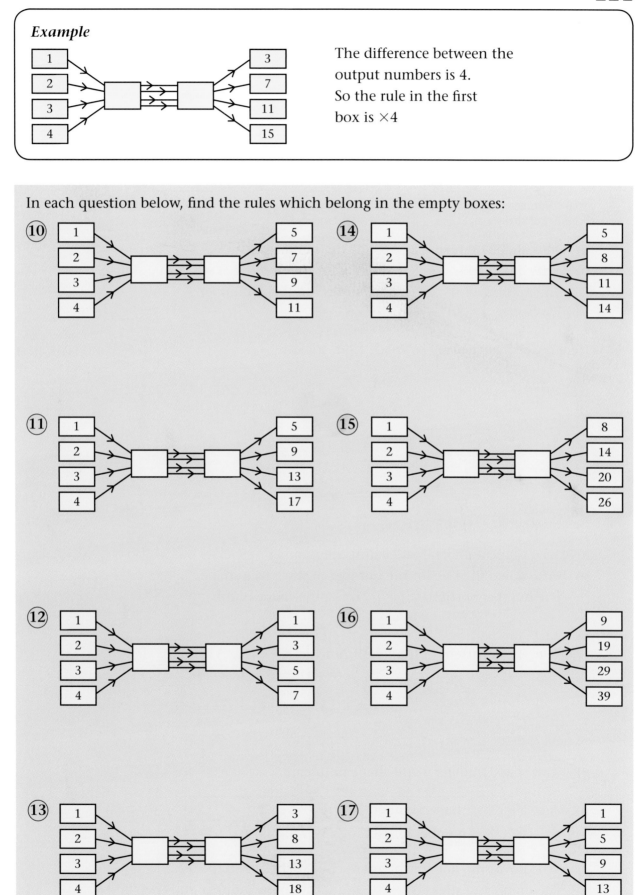

The difference between the output numbers is 4.
So the rule in the first box is ×4

In each question below, find the rules which belong in the empty boxes:

10 — Inputs: 1, 2, 3, 4 → Outputs: 5, 7, 9, 11

11 — Inputs: 1, 2, 3, 4 → Outputs: 5, 9, 13, 17

12 — Inputs: 1, 2, 3, 4 → Outputs: 1, 3, 5, 7

13 — Inputs: 1, 2, 3, 4 → Outputs: 3, 8, 13, 18

14 — Inputs: 1, 2, 3, 4 → Outputs: 5, 8, 11, 14

15 — Inputs: 1, 2, 3, 4 → Outputs: 8, 14, 20, 26

16 — Inputs: 1, 2, 3, 4 → Outputs: 9, 19, 29, 39

17 — Inputs: 1, 2, 3, 4 → Outputs: 1, 5, 9, 13

1 Here is a sequence of triangles made from sticks.

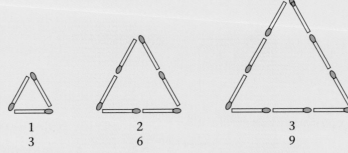

Shape number: 1   2   3
Number of sticks: 3   6   9

a) Draw shape number 4 and count the number of sticks.

b) Write down and complete the rule for the number of sticks in a shape:

'The number of sticks is _____ times the shape number'.

2 Here is a sequence of 'steps' made from sticks.

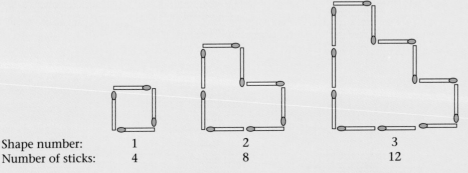

Shape number: 1   2   3
Number of sticks: 4   8   12

a) Draw shape number 4 and count the number of sticks.

b) Write down the rule for the number of sticks in a shape.

'The number of sticks is _____ times the shape number'.

3 Louise makes a pattern of triangles from sticks.

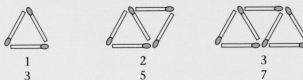

Shape number: 1   2   3
Number of sticks: 3   5   7

a) Draw shape number 4 and shape number 5.

b) Make a table:

shape number	1	2	3	4	5
number of sticks	3	5	7		

c) Write down the rule for the number of sticks in a shape.

'The number of sticks is _____ times the shape number and then add _____'.

On these pages you will read and plot coordinates in all four quadrants.

Ⓜ

① Write down the co-ordinates of the letters.

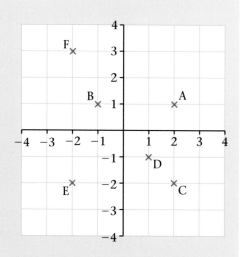

② Draw a grid like the one above.
Plot the points for shape A.
Join them up in the order given.
Use a different colour for each shape.

A	B	C	D
(2, 1)	(−3, −2)	(−4, −3)	(1, 2)
(2, 4)	(2, −2)	(−1, 3)	(−2, 2)
(−3, 4)	(−2, 1)	(2, −3)	(−2, −1)
(−3, 1)	(−3, 1)		(1, −1)

③ Use the grid to work out the joke written in co-ordinates. Work across the page.

(2, −1) (1, −3) (−2, 3) (0, 2)   (3, 2) (1, 3)

(−3, 0) (−1, −3) (0, −1) (0, −1) (1, 0) (2, −1)   (−2, 3) (2, 3) (2, −2)

(−1, −3) (2, 2) (0, 2) (1, −2) (−1, −3) (3, −1) (−1, −3) (0, −1) (−3, 0)

(2, −2) (−2, 3) (2, 3) (−3, 1) (−1, −3) (1, −2) (1, 0) (−2, 1) (1, 3)?

(1, 3) (1, −3) (−2, 3) (1, −2) (−2, −1)

(3, 2) (2, 3) (−1, 0) (−1, −3) (1, 3) (0, 2) (−1, −3) (2, −2)

(2, 1) (−2, 1) (1, 3) (0, 2) (−2, 3) (1, −2) (2, −2)

④ Write down the co-ordinates of the six letters in this grid.

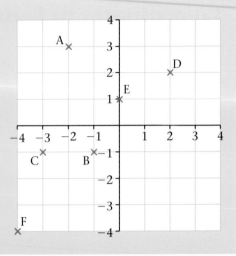

E

Copy the grid below.
Label across from −6 to 10 (horizontal axis).
Label up from −6 to 16 (vertical axis).

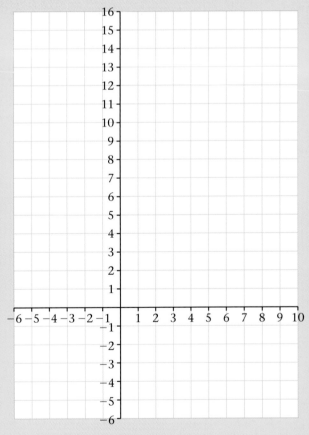

Plot the points below and join them up with a ruler in the order given.

(4, 2)	(4, 4)	(2, 6)	(0, 6)	(−1, 4)	(−1, 2)	(0, 1)
(2, 1)	(4, 2)	(6, 2)	(6, 1)	(5, 1)		

ON THE SAME PICTURE plot the points below and join them up with a ruler in the order given.

DO NOT JOIN THE LAST POINT IN THE BOX ABOVE WITH THE FIRST POINT IN THE NEW BOX.

| $(-3, 13)$ | $(-3, 1)$ | $(-2, 1)$ |

ON THE SAME PICTURE plot the points below and join them up with a ruler in the order given.

| $(0, -4)$ | $(-2, -3)$ | $(-2, -1)$ | $(-4, -1)$ | $(-4, 1)$ | $(-3, 1)$ |

ON THE SAME PICTURE plot the points below and join them up with a ruler in the order given.

| $(3, -5)$ | $(4, -5)$ | $(5, -4)$ | $(4, -3)$ | $(4, -2)$ | $(3, -2)$ |
| $(-1, -1)$ | $(-1, -2)$ | $(1, -3)$ | $(1, -1\frac{1}{2})$ |

ON THE SAME PICTURE plot the points below and join them up with a ruler in the order given.

| $(4, -3)$ | $(1, -3)$ | $(3, -3)$ | $(3, -2)$ | $(7, -2)$ | $(7, 1)$ |
| $(6, 1)$ | $(7, 1)$ | $(8, 2)$ | $(8, 4)$ | $(7, 6)$ |

ON THE SAME PICTURE plot the points below and join them up with a ruler in the order given.

| $(-3, -1)$ | $(-3, -6)$ | $(-4, -6)$ | $(6, -6)$ | $(4, -6)$ | $(4, -5)$ |

ON THE SAME PICTURE plot the points below and join them up with a ruler in the order given.

$(4, 4)$	$(5, 6)$	$(7, 6)$	$(7, 13)$	$(6, 14)$	$(6, 13)$	$(5, 14)$
$(5, 13)$	$(4, 14)$	$(4, 13)$	$(3, 14)$	$(3, 13)$	$(2, 14)$	$(1\frac{1}{2}, 13)$	$(\frac{1}{2}, 14)$
$(0, 13)$	$(-1, 14)$	$(-1, 13)$	$(-2, 14)$	$(-2, 13)$	$(-3\frac{1}{2}, 14)$	$(-3, 13)$

| Draw a ● at $(1, 4)$ and a ● at $(6, 4)$ |

Who am I?   Colour me in?

On these pages you will learn to calculate angles on a straight line, at a point and in a triangle.

Examples

- **ANGLES ON A STRAIGHT LINE**
  The sum of the angles on a straight line is 180°.

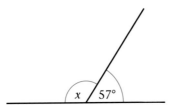

$$x + 57° = 180°$$
$$x = 123°$$

- **ANGLES AT A POINT**
  A whole turn is 360°.

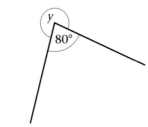

$$y + 80° = 360°$$
$$y = 280°$$

- **ANGLES IN A TRIANGLE**
  The sum of the angles in a triangle is 180°.

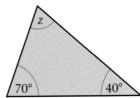

$$z + 110° = 180°$$
$$z = 70°$$

Ⓜ

Find the angles marked with the letters.

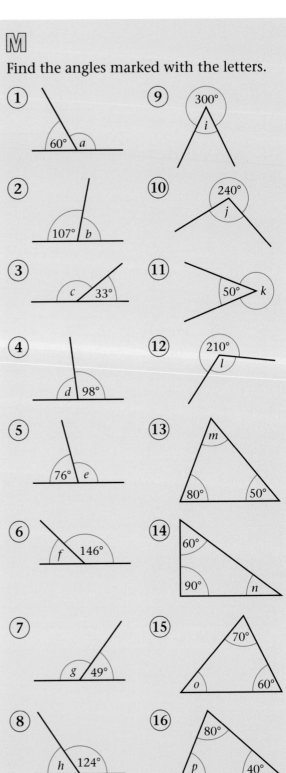

① 60° a

② 107° b

③ c 33°

④ d 98°

⑤ 76° e

⑥ f 146°

⑦ g 49°

⑧ h 124°

⑨ 300° i

⑩ 240° j

⑪ 50° k

⑫ 210° l

⑬ m 80° 50°

⑭ 60° 90° n

⑮ 70° o 60°

⑯ 80° p 40°

E

Find the angles marked with the letters.

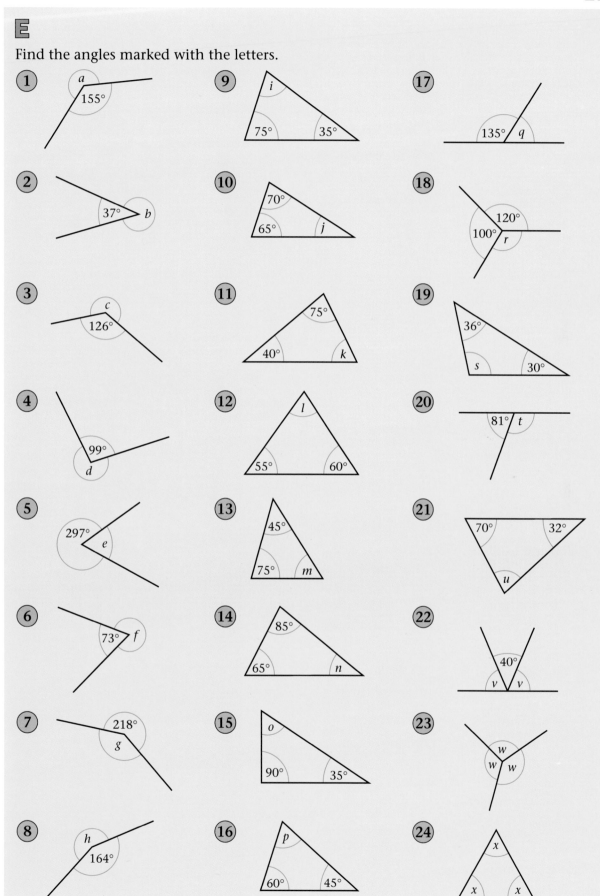

(1) a 155°

(2) 37° b

(3) c 126°

(4) 99° d

(5) 297° e

(6) 73° f

(7) 218° g

(8) h 164°

(9) i 75°   35°

(10) 70°   65° j

(11) 75°   40° k

(12) l 55°   60°

(13) 45°   75° m

(14) 85°   65° n

(15) o 90°   35°

(16) p 60°   45°

(17) 135° q

(18) 120°   100° r

(19) 36° s 30°

(20) 81° t

(21) 70°   32° u

(22) 40° v v

(23) w w w

(24) x x x

On these pages you will learn to make nets for 3-D shapes.

Which of these nets will make an open cube?

①   ②   ③   ④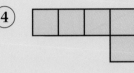

Copy the nets onto squared paper. Draw flaps. Cut them out and see if you were right.

There are 8 different nets for an open cube. Find as many as you can.

⑤ Copy this net onto squared paper.
Remember to draw flaps.
Cut it out and make the cuboid.

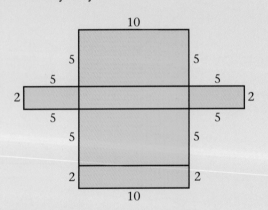

⑥ Make nets for these cuboids.

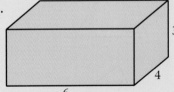   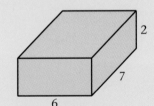

⑦ Copy this net opposite onto squared paper.
Draw flaps, cut it out and make the pyramid.

⑧ Use triangle dotty paper.
Make this net for a tetrahedron.

Can you find a different net that
makes a tetrahedron?

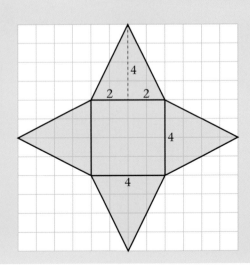

E

Ask your teacher for cardboard.

(1) Draw this square in the middle of the cardboard. All lengths are in cm.

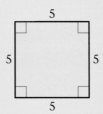

(2) Use a ruler and protractor to draw this triangle joined to your square.

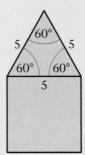

(3) Use a ruler and protractor to draw 3 more triangles joined to your square.

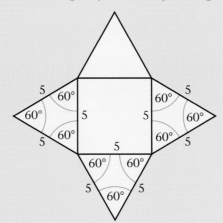

(4) Draw on some flaps like this:

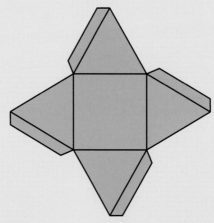

(5) Cut out, fold and glue to make a square based pyramid.

(6) Use a ruler and protractor to draw this net: All lengths are in cm.

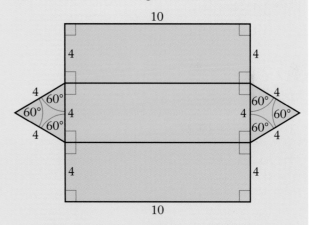

Draw on some flaps.
Cut out, fold and glue to make a triangular prism.

(7) If you have time, think of your own solid and try to make it.

On this page you will learn to interpret the display on a calculator and to solve problems.

Ⓜ

1. 26 − 41
2. 1031 − 48
3. 19 × 75
4. 14 − 57
5. 235 − 86
6. 27 + 64 002
7. 17 − 93
8. 43 − 78
9. £3·20 + 64p
10. £4·90 + 85p

11. £6·00 − 75p − 38p
12. £9·00 − 59p − 64p
13. £2·24 × 15
14. £4·35 × 8
15. £50·40 ÷ 14
16. £31·20 ÷ 12
17. 3·12 + (6·72 × 4)
18. 15·67 + (9·37 × 9)
19. 5 × (2·46 + 1·34)
20. 6 × (12·1 − 5·6)

21. A supermarket needs 10 000 apples.
    A crate holds 48 apples.
    How many crates does the supermarket need to order?

22. Pot plants cost £2·50. How many plants can be bought with £14?

23. A school hall can fit 20 chairs into one row.
    How many rows are needed to seat 312 parents for the school concert?

Ｅ

Copy and complete.

1. 1·37 + ☐ = 2·6
2. 2·58 + ☐ = 4·19
3. ☐ + 0·86 = 4·35
4. ☐ + 1·64 = 3·28
5. 3·45 − ☐ = 1·7
6. 5·28 − ☐ = 3·61
7. ☐ − 1·63 = 0·79
8. ☐ − 2·37 = 1·85

9. Find three consecutive numbers which add up to:
   a) 81   c) 195
   b) 114   d) 222.

10. Tickets for a charity concert cost £4·50. 629 people attend the concert. How much money is raised by the sale of tickets?

11. A lake is 127 metres deep. The surface of the lake is 73 metres above sea level.
    How many metres below sea level is the bottom of the lake?

12. A burger bar sells 276 burgers. The takings for the burgers is £372·60.
    How much does each burger cost?

① Work out 70% of £40

②

Computer £800

SALE

20% off

a) How much is the price of the computer reduced by?

b) What is the sale price?

③ Change 0·07 into a fraction.

④ Change 60% into a decimal.

⑤ a) Measure this angle with a protractor.

b) What is the name of this type of angle?

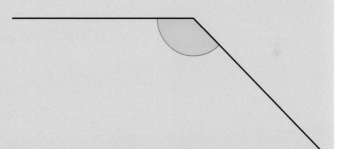

⑥ £6·52 is divided equally between 4 children. How much does each child get?

⑦ 4 children can sit at a table. How many tables are needed to seat 27 children in a class?

⑧ What rule belongs in the empty box below?

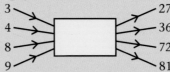

$$3 \rightarrow 27$$
$$4 \rightarrow 36$$
$$8 \rightarrow 72$$
$$9 \rightarrow 81$$

⑨ Find the value of a if

$$3a + 2 = 14$$

⑩ Look at the balancing scales below. Write down the value of x.

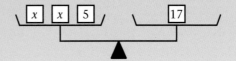

x x 5 17

(11) 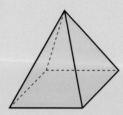 This is a pyramid with a square base (a square on the bottom). **Sketch** a possible **net** to make this pyramid.

(12) What rule belongs in the empty box?

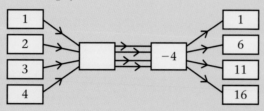

(Clue: the rule is ×?)

(13) Write down the rules which belong in the empty boxes.

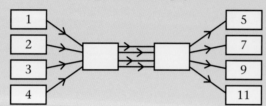

(14) Find the size of angle a below.
Do **not** use a protractor (angle measurer).

Not to scale.

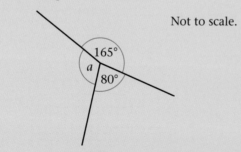

(15)

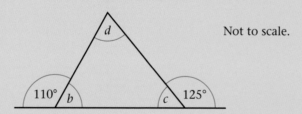

Not to scale.

Work out the size of angle b, angle c and angle d above. Do **not** use a protractor (angle measurer).

(16) If a = 4 and b = 6, find the value of

$$5a + 2b$$

(17) If $c = 6$ and $d = 8$, find the value of

$$5(d - c)$$

(18) Use a calculator to work out

$$\sqrt{225} + \sqrt{361}$$

(19) Use a calculator to work out

$$7 \times (4\cdot81 + 6\cdot3)$$

(20)

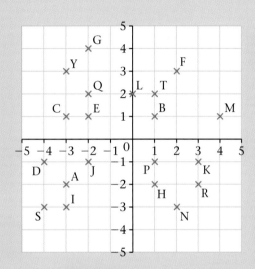

Write down the letter at each of the following co-ordinates to make a word.

$$(-2, 1) \qquad (2, -3) \qquad (-4, -1)$$

On this page you will try to complete crossnumber puzzles.

Copy each crossnumber puzzle onto squared paper.

Use the clues to complete the puzzles.

A

Clues across	Clues down
(1) 9×4	(1) $3170 \div 10$
(3) $107 - 40$	(2) 31×2
(5) $12{\cdot}8 \times 10$	(4) $98 - 21$
(7) 9×5	(6) $58 + 26$
(10) $42 \div 2$	(8) $600 - 75$
(12) $38 + 19$	(9) 9×3
(13) $200 \div 4$	(11) $100 \div 10$

B

Clues across	Clues down
(1) $502 - 104$	(1) $0{\cdot}35 \times 100$
(3) 6×9	(2) $633 + 350$
(5) $82 - 24$	(3) $112 \div 2$
(6) $76{\cdot}2 \times 10$	(4) $387 + 39$
(7) $316 + 46$	(6) 12×6
(11) $0{\cdot}43 \times 100$	(8) 8^2
(13) 41×5	(9) $296 - 48$
(15) $963 - 71$	(10) $3001 - 2894$
(16) $150 \div 2$	(12) $124 - 85$
	(14) $5500 \div 100$

C

Clues across	Clues down
(1) 8×59	(1) $196 \div 4$
(4) 13×7	(2) $689 + 97$
(6) $1002 - 18$	(3) 20×12
(7) $300 \div 5$	(4) $9600 \div 100$
(8) $6080 \div 10$	(5) $4003 - 2994$
(11) $1000 - 251$	(9) $174 \div 2$
(13) $9{\cdot}24 \times 100$	(10) 79×5
(15) $1000 \div 20$	(12) $385 + 57$
(16) 11^2	(14) $320 \div 16$